Praise for
Lifelong Running

"Ruth Heidrich is an inspiration to so many people. Her persistence, her commitment to fitness, her use of the healthiest food, and her consciousness of what could be a bright future for all of us make this book a must read."

—**T. Colin Campbell**, Ph.D.,
Professor Emeritus of Nutrition, Cornell University,
bestselling co-author of *The China Study* and author of *Whole*

"If you've ever wondered whether running might create more joy and vibrant health in your life, this is the book you need to read. Ruth Heidrich most definitely knows what she's talking about. She's a cancer thriver (not just survivor) who has, since her diagnosis, completed nearly a hundred triathlons and more than sixty-six marathons. And this marvelous book also features the voice of Martin Rowe, a fascinating writer who is a former (and still is at times) couch potato, and as such relates very well to those of us who are, for whatever reasons, reluctant to run. Whether you are new to running, or have some experience with the sport, you'll find this extraordinary book to be reassuring, informative, and inspiring."

—**John Robbins**, author of *Diet for a New America*
and co-founder of the Food Revolution Network

"I've been moving a lot faster—and happily so—since reading *Lifelong Running*. This book changed my perception. For one thing, I notice that kids really do run everywhere, and smile while they are doing so. Plus I am looking at running in a new way, as something I can do and want to try. Ruth Heidrich ably shreds the myths that keep people from running at all ages, but especially once their twenties are a memory. She shares her health challenges, exhilaration in moving and exploring, and pleasure in her simple plant-based diet. Her inspiring adventures are complemented by Martin Rowe's account of his journey as a runner and insights into the world of this sport. This book can lead the way to health transformation through a running program at any age, fueled by the optimal plant-powered diet."

    —**Janice Stanger**, Ph.D., author of *The Perfect Formula Diet*

"Ruth's life and writing are an inspiration to millions. This book is yet another gift from her that will get your body moving in ways that will put a smile on your face for the rest of your life."

    —**Mike Anderson**, author of *The RAVE Diet & Lifestyle*

"If longevity and good health are what you're after, Ruth Heidrich has the recipe for them. Her story will not only inspire you, but follow her prescription and you might just get an extra decade of good living out of it."

    —**Kathy Freston**, author of
Quantum Wellness Cleanse, Veganist, and *The Lean*

LIFELONG RUNNING

Overcome the 11 Myths about Running and Live a Healthier Life

Ruth Heidrich, PH.D.
with Martin Rowe

Lantern Books | *New York*
A DIVISION OF BOOKLIGHT INC.

2013
Lantern Books
128 Second Place
Brooklyn, NY 11231
www.lanternbooks.com

The authors of *Lifelong Running* recommend that before
you make any choices about your diet or undertake any fitness
regimen you consult your doctor. None of the advice in this
book should be considered a substitute for a thorough
physical check-up by a practicing physician.

Printed in the United States of America

Library of Congress Cataloging-in-Publication Data

Heidrich, Ruth.
Lifelong running : overcome the 11 myths about running
and live a healthier life / Ruth Heidrich, Ph.D., Martin Rowe.
pages cm
Includes bibliographical references.
ISBN 978-1-59056-385-4 (pbk. : alk. paper) —
ISBN 978-1-59056-386-1 (ebook)
1. Running. 2. Running—Training. 3. Running—Health aspects.
4. Running—Physiological aspects. I. Rowe, Martin. II. Title.
GV1061.H375 2013
613.7'172—dc23
2013015523

CONTENTS

CONTENTS

FOREWORD

Martin Rowe

In 2006, after more than two decades of comfortable inactivity on various plush couches in Great Britain and the United States, I decided to run a marathon. A gang of very persuasive reasons had conspired in a dark corner of my life to persuade me to agree to their well-articulated demands.

The first was that my metabolism had slowed and I was beginning to suffer from what my wife calls "married-man belly." This condition afflicts many people of the male persuasion. We suck in our stomachs, scrub our fingernails, and clip our nose hairs in an effort to render ourselves attractive enough to snare a spouse. Once we've done so, we then leave our hair unwashed, eat a diet that causes hardened nutritionists to shudder, and gallantly accompany our expanding waistline to the easy chair where we devote the next forty years to contemplating our inner beauty, rapier wit, and well-developed sense of irony.

For my wife, ever the moralist, married-man belly was not merely the inevitable consequence of my reclining too long on the couch (without even a few neurasthenic sonnets to justify it), but an affront to common decency. If, she reasoned with her usual forceful clarity, she was going to spend precious hours making herself presentable to the world, the least I could do was to lift my butt from the extremely inviting cushions and wiggle my limbs a bit. "Deal with it," she said, more or less lovingly. "And I don't mean that metaphorically."

I knew myself well enough to discern that, if I were to get rid of the offending flab, it wouldn't do, like a contemporary Sisyphus, to run forever on the incline of a treadmill. Nor would I be content solely to climb an endless StairMaster®, like some forlorn denizen of an M. C. Escher etching. I needed a goal—and that goal, I decided, would be to run a marathon. I'd seen people whom I considered perfectly sane and respectable run one, and do so in a sane and respectable time. These individuals were, to put it mildly, neither particularly athletic nor ferociously Spartan in their discipline, and yet they'd managed to complete the miles without keeling over or otherwise causing any obvious harm to themselves or their loved ones. If they could do it, why couldn't I?

Another kick in the pants was delivered (thankfully, not literally) by the co-author of this book: Ruth Heidrich. Ruth's *A Race for Life* had been the first title my publishing company, Lantern Books, had issued (in 2000), and the story of how she'd recovered from a double mastectomy following a diagnosis of breast cancer at the age of forty-seven by completing four Ironman Triathlons in a year knocked me sideways (also, thankfully, not literally). Ruth's boundless enthusiasm and total commitment to life were impossible to ignore, as were her achievements: a hundred triathlons, sixty-six marathons, a resting heart-rate of forty-four beats a minute, the bone mass of a thirty-year-old woman, and so on.

As a further incentive, Lantern produced in 2005 another of Ruth's books, *Senior Fitness*, which extolled the virtues of physical activity well into one's seventh, eighth, and even ninth decades. But why did I need to wait thirty years to start exercising? I was in my forties like Ruth when she completed her first Ironman. Unlike her, I didn't to my knowledge have any life-threatening illnesses, and most of my body parts remained intact. If Ruth could swim 2.4 miles, ride 112 miles on a bicycle, and then run a marathon—and do that *four* times in the space of twelve months while recovering from breast cancer—then it shouldn't be that hard to do only the final portion of the race . . . *once*.

I really had no excuse for such torpor, especially since I hadn't always been recumbent. I'd been quite competitive at ball games as a boy in England (cricket, tennis, soccer, squash, etc.) and had possessed decent enough hand–eye coordination to be chosen for my school sides. I'd made two attempts to play cricket with local teams in New York City. However, while the games had been sociologically interesting, they'd left me feeling very sore and out of sorts and not eager to repeat the experience. I'd had to endure an endless subway ride and a car journey simply to get to the grounds where the matches took place—and these games sometimes lasted six hours. Theoretically, all I had to do to begin running was to step outside of my house, and I could go as fast or slow for as long or short a distance as I wanted.

I was finding it hard to come up with excuses *not* to run. I hadn't taken part in formal athletics since I was about thirteen years old, but I'd been good enough for a teacher to comment in my hearing as I ran around a four-hundred-yard track that I "could run across Africa." As it turned out, whether to spite the schoolmaster or because I just didn't believe him, or maybe because Africa at that moment seemed too large a continent for too small a boy, I'd dropped out of the race, and hadn't run since. I'd had some ability as a child: Why couldn't I capture that again? I might not be one of the million or so wildebeest or zebras traversing the Masai Mara or Serengeti—although we *were* all herbivores. But even without the incentive of being chased by a pack of lions, I could at least try to trot forty-two kilometers.

And so it came to pass that, after much navel-gazing and futzing around, Lazarus-like I rose from the sofa and entered the lottery to run the 2006 New York City Marathon. To my surprise, since I'd never to my knowledge won a lottery before, I was accepted. I began to run and almost immediately injured myself doing stupid things that I'll talk about later in this book. I exercised the option of paying the fee again and postponing my initiation to the following year, and as part of my training took part in several of the races organized by New York Road Runners (NYRR). Founded in 1958, the NYRR (www.nyrr.org) has become an association with many tens of thousands of members. It stages a wide variety of races, including half-marathons, long training runs, four- and five-milers, and 10Ks throughout the year, sponsored by various consulates, medical charities, and nonprofits. Since 1970, its signature event has been the New York City Marathon, which is held on the first Sunday in November. (I write about the race in the Interlude, which you'll find between chapters eight and nine.)

I took to my training regimen with my usual doggedness and lack of flair, and come November 2007 I managed to complete the race in a time of three hours and fifty-eight minutes, which I considered respectable for a first effort. Since then, to my considerable surprise, I've run thirteen more marathons—four more New York City ones; two each in Miami, Chicago, and New Jersey; one in Boston; one in the great borough of Brooklyn; and the Sri Chinmoy Self-Transcendence Marathon, which consisted of a Dantesque circumambulation of no fewer than nine circuits of Rockland Lake State Park in upstate New York. My personal best is 3:28, which is just this side of *not bad* for my age and sex. I've also completed over twenty half-marathons (personal best, 1:34), along with many other shorter races.

When I told my friends in 2007 that I'd discovered an interest in distance running, they were so astonished and incredulous that I, so dedicated to a life in repose, had decided to run a marathon that they donated $11,500 to my chosen cause—the Woodstock Farm Animal Sanctuary. They kindly hid their annoyance that I failed to make that marathon a one-off venture, and have shrewdly come up with reasons why they've given less and less each time I've run for charity ("What about a triathlon?" "What about an ultra?" "When are you going to break three hours?"). I've ignored their efforts to up the ante and to irritate them further have taken to calling myself, with all the self-righteousness I can muster, "a marathoner."

Although I'm in no danger of troubling the record keepers, and truthfully find my late-in-life commitment to *la vie sportive* somewhat absurd, I actually enjoy it. I'm a great watcher of training videos on the Web—some of whose expertise I've handed on in this book. I was engrossed by *Run for Your Life*, the documentary film about the transplanted Transylvanian Fred Lebow, the towering figure behind the New York City Marathon (and, indeed, all recreational running in New York).[1] I even shed a tear or two when, toward the end of the movie, Lebow, in remission from the brain cancer that would eventually kill him, finally ran the race that he'd helped turn into the biggest single public sporting event in the world.

In 2011, I was surprised at how deeply affected I was by the death from cancer of Grete Waitz, the Norwegian Olympian, world-record holder, and nine-time winner of the New York City Marathon. She was only fifty-seven years old. Waitz had been Lebow's running companion that day in 1992 when they'd crossed the finish line together in 5:32:34 (a time that was as difficult to achieve for Waitz as it was for Lebow, for opposite reasons). The runner and the organizer had turned the New York City Marathon into a major international occasion. Waitz's cool brilliance and dedication to helping even the humblest of plodders made her one of the most inspirational of all long-distance runners. I felt as though I *knew* her—even though I wouldn't have recognized her five years previously. In fact, I'd only seen her on four occasions, a slight figure in a tracksuit standing on the podium, waving us off at the beginning of the October half-marathon that was named in her honor.

To this day, I continue to be intrigued by the articles in *Runner's World* and *NY Runner*—two magazines I didn't know existed, let alone thought would hold any interest for me, before I took up the sport. I'm fascinated by split times and iliotibial bands, and will talk to anyone with a bandana and a Garmin™ watch about compression socks and personal bests and how it is they don't spill the water they pick up from the hydration tables. (You pinch the cup so the opening forms a narrow chute down which the water runs into your mouth, in case you wanted to know. It's harder to do than you'd think when you're not walking.) In fact, if there were a championship for Official Running Bore, I'd place every time. I guess running does this to you.

I presume I'm now in finer fettle than at any time in the past twenty years, although my struggle against married-man belly continues. My wife still considers the amount of time I spend studying the twill on the divan exorbitant (although those aren't her precise words). But at least I now have a defense: I'm resting from many hours spent careering through the streets of major metropolitan areas in search of the elusive elixir of complete health and youth. Or something to that effect.

Since the mid-1980s, when Ruth became an Ironman athlete *and* a vegan, and especially in the last few years, running among those who eschew meat and dairy has become almost de rigueur. Scott Jurek, Rich Roll, and Brendan Brazier—all ultramarathon champions—have demonstrated not only that you can be a vegan *and* run scores of miles, but that you can outpace and outlast anyone, including omnivores. Many of my vegan acquaintances now regularly run marathons and compete in triathlons, at speeds and in times that put me to shame; others run shorter races and regularly pick up prizes for placing in their age-group. We owe Ruth and other pioneers a huge debt of thanks for showing us that a commitment to our own good health doesn't have to be at the expense of the good health of other animals' bodies.

While Ruth and I are both vegans, we are so for different reasons. Ruth chose her diet as part of her recovery from a cancer diagnosis and to maintain maximal bodily health; I chose mine, many years before I started running, because of my concerns over animal welfare and the negative environmental effects of intensive animal agriculture. Ruth is also inclined to eat more raw food than I am—perhaps a conse-quence of the fact that she lives in the fruitarian paradise of Hawaii and I dwell amid the decidedly seasonal pleasures of Brooklyn, New York. Both of us, however, firmly believe that one should eat as little processed food as possible. We also agree that although you'll certainly gain benefits from running without becoming a vegan, adopting the diet will not only *not* limit your performance but you'll be doing a lot of good for yourself, the planet, and the creatures with whom we share it.

Lifelong Running is first and foremost Ruth's book. She's the inspi-ration behind my running, and, indeed, one of the mothers of the company that published it. It was, therefore, a double delight not only that she agreed to my suggestion that she distill a lifetime's knowledge on the subject into a book for Lantern, but that she has allowed me to provide, quite literally, a running commentary (I'm the *M.R.* you'll read every now and then). I freely admit that I'm not as hardcore as Ruth, both in running and in my diet, and that I tend to take a more cerebral, even worrywartish approach to an activity that, as you'll see throughout *Lifelong Running*, Ruth finds as natural and life-affirming as breathing. That we're such different characters, perhaps at opposite ends of the spectrum of attitudes toward this activity, illustrates how broadly it's possible to construe what it means to be a runner. Quite simply, that there are as many *ways* to run as *people* to do it.

More than anything else, *Lifelong Running* amply demonstrates that moving one's body more quickly than walking isn't necessarily the pursuit of the young and the reckless. Nor do you have to run any or many marathons or triathlons or Ironman races to acquire pleasure, a sense of accomplishment, and the numerous health benefits that running provides you with. So, although Ruth and I spend a lot of time talking about long-distance races in this book, you shouldn't feel that running only becomes worthy of the name when you deplete your stores of glycogen or your toenails fall off. Start with a jog down the block. You'll find, as Ruth and I did, that before you know it, you'll have entered your first 5K race, and then a 10K, and then a half-marathon. And then it's over; you're hooked!

But before you lace up those shoes and head out the door, settle back and enjoy the couch with Ruth and me for just a little longer. After all, lifelong running should be accompanied by lifelong reading.

INTRODUCTION

As the cruise ship pulled into the Sydney Harbour Bay, I was topside on the jogging track, running around and around as each circuit presented new views of the two world-famous icons of Down Under. On the port side were the white sails of the Sydney Opera House and, to the starboard, the Sydney Harbour Bridge. The bridge looked so high and magnificent that I decided that as soon as the ship docked, I was going to run across it.

As it turned out, the road leading from the dock toward the bridge did a U-turn, and I found myself on the other side from where the bridge started. Dismayed, I looked around but couldn't see the road leading up, way up, to the traffic crossing the bridge. Spying a young man I guessed was a local resident, I stopped and asked him how I could get up to the bridge. Looking a bit surprised, he said that if I continued a bit further, I'd see a road to the left. Grinning, I carried on, but breathed a lot harder on the rise up the steep hill. When I reached the top, I was heady with excitement, marveling at the beautiful sight: the structure of the bridge itself, all the boats in the harbor down below, and, of course, the opera house.

I started my run across the bridge, recalling the time I ran across the Golden Gate Bridge in San Francisco. At the time, I thought that was pretty exciting and brave of me. But this! This was ten times better because, after all, I was in Australia. So when I got to the other side of the span, I turned around and headed back, thinking what a shame it was that I hadn't been able to find anyone to run with me—and now, no one to share this exciting moment with.

Then I remembered—my little digital camera was tucked in my waist-pack. I really wanted to get a photo of this experience. But who was going to take it? Fortunately, just at that moment I saw a young lady walking toward me. She said she'd love to take a picture of me running across the bridge. As a result, I'm now able to show people that photograph and share that wonderful moment.

I'm relating this anecdote to you now because that's what running means to me. It's a way for me to see the world, both the one on the outside and the one on the inside—how my body works and how to keep it healthy. I hope to have this unique perspective for the rest of my life. I know I will as long as I keep running. But, like many of you reading this book, I didn't start out that way.

How and Why I Started Running

Back in 1968, I happened to pass a magazine stand and noticed a paperback book with a strange title—*Aerobics*—a word I'd never seen before. In fact, the word had just been coined by the author, Kenneth Cooper, M.D. Curious, I stopped to see what the book was about. First, Cooper's definition of aerobics was any exercise done at a level that enabled one to get enough oxygen, as characterized by the "talk test." If you could talk while running and not be out of breath, you were doing something "aerobic." As I thumbed through the pages, I noticed how each chapter referred to different parts of the body: how they got diseased from lack of exercise and how to get them well again. From bad backs to insomnia to flat feet, I had them all! Although I was only thirty-three at the time, I had serious back problems—two herniated discs—and had been told I needed surgery to remove the discs and fuse three vertebrae in the lumbar region. I was also noticing signs of aging—the start of some varicose veins, a bit of flabbiness here, a little more there. . . .

I thought that *Aerobics* might be a very interesting book and so I bought it and read it from cover to cover in a single sitting. I learned that Dr. Cooper's research demonstrated how exercise that stressed the body to the point of breathing hard and sweating made it stronger from top to bottom—and all those body parts in between. The whole concept intrigued me and I was all set to try it out.

The next morning I woke up extra early, dug into the back of my closet, and found an old T-shirt, a pair of cuffed Bermuda shorts, and my old tennis shoes. I tiptoed out the front door and tentatively started running down the street. I remember thinking that it was a good thing it was still dark, because I would have been very embarrassed if anyone had seen me. (Remember, this was back in the 1960s when anyone running was either trying to catch a departing bus or being chased by the cops!) When I reached the end of my street, I turned around and headed for home. I was hot and sweaty so I jumped into our swimming pool, swam a few laps to cool down, and beamed. I had just run a whole mile and loved how it made me feel: strong, independent, healthy, and fit. I was almost going to be late for work, so I quickly got dressed and headed out the door, noting that I seemed to have more energy—not less, which is what I would have expected. I was smiling the whole time at work, thinking about my little secret and how great I felt.

The next day I decided to do the same thing, and the day after, and the day after. . . . I've had a nearly perfect running streak since 1968. It became part of my normal morning routine: wake up, do some minimal morning ablutions, put on my running clothes, and head out the door. What I discovered was that by running first thing in the morning, nothing ever interfered with it. It set me up for the whole day, and the rewards were increased fitness, a greater appetite that could be satisfied without my gaining weight, a lot more energy all day long, and a nice, deep, restful sleep. This routine lasted until I got the shock of my life in 1982—the diagnosis of breast cancer.

How I Became an Ironman

At the time I was diagnosed with cancer, I'd been a runner for fourteen years and had even run a number of marathons. I was totally devastated, shocked, scared, and angry, thinking that I'd been betrayed by my body. Recovering from my cancer surgery, I'd not yet gone back to work and couldn't do much running, and so had time to while away. I never before had occasion to watch much television, but now there wasn't much else to do. While channel surfing, I happened to come across one of the most famous incidents in sports history.

What I saw was runner Julie Moss *crawling* to the Ironman Triathlon finish line in 1982 in total exhaustion, her body starting to shut down—and she was in first place. Watching her heroic effort made me realize that I was facing a similar crisis in my own life. Here I was, one day a marathoner and the next day a cancer patient! I looked at my life knowing I could die from disease in a matter of months. I then decided that I was going to fight it with every weapon I could think of. The first weapon was a change of diet, which I'll talk more about later. The second, which I decided right after watching Julie Moss finish, was to do the Ironman.

Then came Reality Check #1. *Lady, you've forgotten you're now a cancer patient*, the thought ran in my head. *You're sick, you could be dying, you've lost everything, there's no way you can do this.* And so on it went. But then . . . *hey, wait a minute, I can still run. I can dig out my old, rusty bike from the garage and start biking. I already know how to swim, so I can handle that, too.*

Reality Check #2: *Lady, you're forty-seven years old. Look at all these competitors—they're all in their twenties, possibly thirties at the most. This is a young person's game, obviously.* My next thought was that maybe I could set some kind of record: "Oldest woman to complete the Ironman!" Or, "First cancer patient to complete the Ironman!" That did it; I had a goal. I was off and running, both literally and figuratively.

I soon discovered that with my new diet, I felt stronger, faster, more energetic, and recovered from workouts much faster, and that by adding the swimming and biking my running benefited. I was getting stronger and fitter from head to toe. All this exercise also had the advantage of keeping me from worrying about the cancer. After all, how could I die if I was feeling the fittest I'd been in my whole life?

My mental outlook soared as well. I knew that training for the Ironman was one of the best decisions I'd ever made.

Because I'd gone back to work, I had to figure out how I was going to get all that training into an already busy schedule. Since I'd been doing hour-long early-morning runs for years, keeping up the running was no problem. Because I lived about six miles from my office and up a very steep hill, I started biking to and from work—the steep hill giving me an extra-hard last mile. A pool was very close to my office, so I swam for the better part of my lunch hour. On weekends I did extra-long runs, bike rides, and swims in the ocean. I also entered every race that came along to give me the motivation and support in the way of aid stations along the course, so I could extend the distances in all three sports.

I knew that I had the marathon-distance runs handled, but this wasn't going to be enough for the grueling 2.4-mile swim and the 112-mile bike ride. I had to prepare myself to keep going through the daunting fatigue I knew I'd face during the actual event, so I did two and three races in one weekend whenever I could and once completed three marathons in three weeks.

I then ran my first ultramarathon, The Run to the Sun, which was thirty-seven miles from sea level at Kahului, Maui, to the top of Mount Haleakala at over 10,000 feet. This run wasn't just over a greater total distance than I'd have to do in the Ironman, it was all uphill—a sure way to get me stronger mentally as well as physically. I recall hitting the aid station at the twenty-six-mile mark, stopping long enough to look down the mountain to the ocean below, marveling at how far I'd come, and thanking my legs for already carrying me for a full marathon. I then turned around, looked up the mountain, and realized I had eleven more miles to go. That's when I remembered why I entered this race—to toughen me up for the Ironman, which was going to take me a lot longer to complete. There were even some fun rewards along the way; I was winning gold medals in each of these races!

As it turned out, my training efforts paid off, although when I found myself at the starting line of the Ironman, I looked around at all those young, fit bodies and wondered why I'd put myself in such a position. On top of it all, just seven weeks before the beginning of the race I'd been hit by a truck during a bike training ride. I'd suffered a fractured pelvis and a concussion. Doctors had told me to forget doing the Ironman; that there was no way I could recover in time to do it. My training had been seriously curtailed, although I'd trained as much as I could in the water, and later on a stationary bike, which was how I still found myself toeing the starting line of the Ironman. I knew I could complete the swim and the bike portion of the race, but the final segment was really questionable, since I hadn't run for those seven weeks. In fact, I'd been on crutches for four of those weeks. That was when I decided that I would walk as far as I could and then drop out.

I discovered that by the time I finished the bike, I had aches and pains all over. I thought that this was it. No more—I quit! But then I remembered that all my gear and my ride was at the finish line at the King Kamehameha Hotel six miles away. I decided to walk back to the hotel. After a few minutes of walking, however, I found I felt strong enough to start running. The further I ran, the better I felt. This was just unbelievable! I reached the hotel and thought I'd just go up as far as the top of the first hill, up to the Queen Kaahumanu Highway. I still felt like I didn't have to quit. Again, I picked another goal, and another, and another, until I realized that I was going to be able to finish the whole race! My time was 14:49, well below the cut-off time of seventeen hours. As I crossed the finish line, I thought to myself, *Just wait until next year when you'll be able to train without having to worry about recovering from injuries.* (Sure enough, the next year I took forty-five minutes off that time, coming in at 14:04.) What amazed me even more was how good I felt after each event and that I was able to do a short run the next day. I attributed my fast recovery to my new diet.

Running Is Fundamental and Primal

I've learned so much about running since my cancer went into remission over thirty years ago and I began competing in triathlons. Exercising in this way may or may not be considered only a sport; for most adults it's an activity that they've long since given up. But running is also one of the most fundamental and primal activities that we humans do, starting from the time we learn to walk. Obviously, running started way before the aerobics boom of the late sixties. To what extent we were distance runners in our early evolutionary history, I'm not sure, but I know we're most successful when we run in groups, as our earliest ancestors must have done. I'm also sure that running has contributed a great deal to our survival as a species.

Unfortunately, our culture has devolved into one where we expect instant gratification—fast foods, quick fixes, and little blue pills—to the problems we face. Rather than changing our lifestyles, most of us would rather take medicine to lose weight, reduce high blood pressure, lower cholesterol, try to control blood sugar, treat erectile dysfunction, tackle heartburn, or knock out the first hint of any pain. We're seldom aware of the insidious side effects of these drugs and the futility of treating symptoms rather than attacking the *cause* of those symptoms. Excess weight, elevated blood pressure, high cholesterol and blood sugar, impotence, heartburn, and pain are almost always symptoms of an unhealthy lifestyle. Evidence is accumulating that dementia is also a lifestyle-related condition, since it's more common in some countries than others. Lack of exercise is a major problem in our sedentary society, and one that's relatively easy to reverse—if you just start running.

Regrettably, persistent myths about running and its effects on our body put off many would-be runners. Most of these myths are cited by non-runners. However, I do occasionally hear them from ex-runners and even physicians. I can't claim I'm right a hundred percent of the time, but I know what's worked for me, what has worked for many others, and I believe it may work for you. In the following pages I attempt to dispel these myths and show you just how healthy, fun, and rewarding running can be.

But I'm Not a Runner!

"If you run, you're a runner. It doesn't matter how far or how fast. It doesn't matter if today is your first day or if you've been running for twenty years. There is no test to pass, no license to earn, no membership card to get. You just run."

—**John Bingham**, marathon runner
and author, also known as "The Penguin"

I'd love to have a dollar for the number of times I've heard "But I'm not a runner!" from folks who find out that I am or when the subject comes up. What they probably mean by their reply is that they've never considered running or that it hurts to do so. They probably have in their minds that unless they look like a Kenyan then there's no point in stepping outside!

What they don't know is that we could all look and be just like Kenyan runners if we lived like they do. Many Kenyan athletes grow up running and, for the most part, never give it up. They never had a bus to take them to and from school. As a result, they run—even though their school might be many miles from home. Some even run home for lunch and then back again. When these students finish their schooling, they find out that a great deal of money and fame can be had if you're one of the fastest runners and can win races. If you're poor and don't have many prospects to make money other than your running expertise, you pour all your efforts into it. Not only can you make a living for yourself, but you may also provide welcome revenue for your family and your entire community.

Because a lot is at stake for young men and women from developing countries, and because of their fame, we have this stereotyped vision of what a "real runner" is, and believe that we have to possess a certain body type to run. But, barring some rare congenital issue, we're all runners—perfectly engineered from birth to run. We're simply out of touch with what we are born to do.

Most people don't realize that it's only when we quit running as children that we become sedentary and weak from hardly walking any distance at all, and start piling on the pounds from the bad diet that most of us Westerners indulge in. Many of us can't even comprehend the joy and bliss from being lean and fit and able to cover miles of beautiful countryside or exploring a new city or town we're visiting.

Scientific Evidence

In findings published in the British journal *Nature,* Harvard University's Daniel Lieberman, PH.D., and his colleagues, who've been studying the evolutionary development of humans in terms of our capacity to run, analyzed the skeletons of humans; animals who run, such as cheetahs, pumas, etc.; and animals who don't run, such as cows, pigs, etc. The researchers found a very different evolution of not just the foot anatomy among these species, but the skeleton all the way up to and including the neck. I was surprised to learn from the study that humans have a structure in our necks, the nuchal ligament, that allows us to turn our heads as we run, and that the non-running animals, such as pigs, do not. Humans also have enough endurance that we can outrun all other animals. True, some can run faster than us for a short distance, but not for as *long*. This evidence suggests that we're truly born to run.[2]

Lieberman *et al.*'s hypothesis is that, as we left the trees and the jungle, we adapted to the changed environment and, thus, became more runners than climbers. In our evolution, we've undergone a number of adaptations, including, as noted earlier, alterations in the neck, pelvis, lower leg, and foot. Out of this research, differences between "barefoot runners"—those who wear minimalist running shoes—and runners with running shoes were noted with differences in efficiency, form, and impact.

Memes

Another translation of the myth "But I'm not a runner!" can also mean "I hate running," with the real subtext being "It just feels good being lazy and not having to exert any effort to get from Point A to Point B." After a few years of not running, most people have lost all their natural inclination to enjoy it the way kids so obviously do. It may take some effort and perhaps even a little discomfort, but our bodies are nothing if not adaptable. In under a minute after we've begun to run our heart-rate increases, our breathing deepens, and our muscles warm up. More blood gets shunted to the working muscles and, by default, to every other part of our body. Within weeks, our bodies actually start looking forward to this infusion of activity. Unfortunately, very few of us are pushed by our parents, friends, doctors, or society in general to start to run in later life because of the idea that running is not good for adults.

All, however, is not lost! The answer to that social resistance may be found in the work of the scientist Dr. Richard Dawkins, who has picked up his studies of genetics and gone a little further. Using the Greek word for imitation, Dawkins has coined the word *meme* to define a unit of *cultural* transmission, rather in the manner that genes are units of *physical* transmission.[3] Memes consist of bits of information, beliefs, attitudes, foregone conclusions, behaviors, and assumptions that we hold in this society and which are so embedded that they're hardly ever questioned. In fact, they're so much a part of our thinking that it's almost impossible to imagine an alternative.

Memes may or may not be valid. For example, what is generally accepted as a valid meme might be "We can't possibly live without indoor plumbing," or "Take an aspirin whenever you get a headache." An example of a false meme is that "All meals need animal protein to be complete," or "Running is a high-impact sport and high impacts are bad for your body."

Memes about the Western lifestyle are so accepted that most people never even think to question their exercise and diet routines. I'm suggesting that for a large percentage of our population, there's no doubt in their minds that running not only isn't healthful but that it can actually harm the body. How else do we explain why runners make up such a small percentage of our population, and why most people don't get any regular exercise at all?

We also know that many people think that eating as much protein as you can is healthful and that animal foods are the best source of that protein. In fact, some people think that the more protein you eat, the better; or that if you want to build a lot of muscle, you have to eat a high-protein diet; or that if you do a lot of running, you need to add extra protein to your diet. Well, you might need more protein if you're a runner, but many people don't stop to think that if you're burning more calories through exercise, you're generally eating more and therefore your protein intake goes up proportionally. You certainly don't need to add animal products or protein powders, because of the harm they may possibly do to the kidneys and bones.

We also know of a number of societies where people rarely eat any meat or dairy and are very healthy, with little or no heart disease, cancer, hypertension, obesity, or the other illnesses that we're prone to. These individuals are also very active, sometimes engage in hard physical labor, and the men can even sire children into their nineties. The wrong diet, along with little or no exercise, is the cause of most deaths by far in Western societies. Strangely, this idea is not a meme.

Another meme goes that runners are a breed apart from the rest of so-called "normal" people. If we can just get these "non-runners" to change that self-image in their minds to "runner," if we can get them to mentally peel off those layers of body fat and start running, they'd find lean, muscular, beautiful "runners" under that skin.

Memes embed themselves so deeply into what we think of as common sense, they nestle so completely into traditions and feelings, that it's difficult for most people even to consider an alternative. Unless and until we change our attitudes toward running and every other type of exercise, however, our society will continue to grow more sedentary, more obese, and more sickly—to the extent that our medical bills will soon bankrupt our economy.

Excuses, Excuses

Getting people to exercise is a real challenge because I think most of us have that "thriftiness" gene. In other words, unless there's an emergency we generally try to get by with doing as little as possible. That explains why, according to National Institutes of Health statistics, only about thirty percent of people ages 45–64 get regular exercise. It gets worse as we get older. From ages 65–74 the average is about twenty-five percent, and for 85+ it's only eleven percent. No wonder we have soaring levels of frailty, osteoporosis, heart disease, diabetes, dementia, and much more. Since most of us already know that regular exercise is important, why don't we do it? Well, here are the most common excuses.

- **I don't have time**. We all have the same twenty-four hours, so it's a matter of priorities. Since most people watch at least some television, it's possible to replace time sitting on the sofa with a nice run. Or you can run in place while watching the evening news. You may also find, as I did, that running gives you *more* energy, so you get more efficient and therefore have more time.
- **I tried it once but quit**. Several techniques can help you over that hump. You can make appointments with yourself on your calendar and make them sacred. Or you can keep a log

of distance, time, and how you felt while you were running. Once you get a string of successes, you just might want to keep going. Set small goals such as "run one block, walk one block," etc. Find an exercise buddy, someone you wouldn't want to let down or disappoint.

- **I'm too tired**. As your fitness increases, you'll find that exercise gives you more energy, as noted earlier. I recommend that you run first thing in the morning when your energy levels are apt to be highest. Also, there's less risk of something coming up to preempt your run. Once your fitness increases, you'll find a definite decrease in feelings of fatigue and even use running to recharge your batteries.

- **I have small children whom I can't leave**. Well, take them with you! Baby joggers are made for that very purpose, and this way you're setting a good example for your children. Kids too old for strollers can ride alongside you on their bikes. They usually really enjoy these outings as well.

- **I just don't like to exercise**. At least this is an honest excuse! Most people resist change in any form, so starting a running program can be a challenge. That's when you need to think about all the rewards that await you. Having a nice, slim, fit body is enough motivation for a lot of people.

The Rewards of Running

What keeps us doing anything in life is the basic reward system. That's one of the first principles of psychology I learned way back in my first university psych class. Its corollary is that we stop doing things that either have no reward or for which we're punished. Elements of both the positive and negative can help in getting us motivated to start a running program. Very frequently, what gets us even thinking about starting a running program—besides knowing it's a "should"—is the vision of a strong, lean body and muscular, good-looking legs. I'll never forget two reminders of that.

At a race one early Sunday morning, my friend Bonnie K. looked at me in mock disgust and said, "You and your thirty-year-old legs!" Except that they were sixty-year-old legs! The second reminder was when I was passing through Jacksonville, Florida, and found out that the Jacksonville Marathon was being run the next day. I was barely into the first mile when I heard a familiar voice behind me. "Ruth! I knew it was you. I'd know those legs anywhere!" It was Frank, a military running buddy from Hawaii who'd gone home on leave and had decided to do that same marathon. It was pretty exciting for me to see an old friend in new territory—and to be recognized by my legs!

Then there are the secondary rewards: more energy, better sleep, time to get away from it all, a method to handle depression, being able to eat more without gaining weight, getting the exercise you know your body needs in an effective and efficient way, and many others.

The bad news is that getting started can be very uncomfortable—your feet hurt, you shins hurt, and your chest hurts. In fact, everything's going to hurt and you'll no doubt experience a period of adjustment as the body adapts to the stresses of a new activity. There's also the fear that people will think you look silly; or that you'll have to buy a bunch of expensive, specialized equipment that you may never use; or that you'll have to get up even earlier than you do already; or even pure procrastination, as in "I'll start *tomorrow*." I suspect that in too many cases these negatives win the mental argument and a running program never even gets off the ground.

In those cases where the positives win, however, there'll soon be the exhilaration of having run your first whole mile. The rewards are losing weight; developing nice, muscular legs; enjoying being in nature; and perhaps best of all, knowing that your body is getting fitter. You'll have a stronger heart; lungs that are more efficient in oxygen extraction; greater muscle development in the torso, butt, legs, and feet; and a brain that thinks more clearly and creatively. If these aren't enough of a reward, I don't know what is!

Run Right for Your Body Type

I'm six feet two inches tall and relatively slender (170 lbs), which one might suppose would make me the "ideal" shape for a runner. However, I've run enough races in my time to conclude that there's actually no perfect body type—at least as far as being a semi-competent and moderately useful athlete goes. One might think that my height would be an advantage because I'm likely to possess a longer stride than a shorter runner. I, too, once thought this and had images of myself cantering around the course like the great four-hundred-meter hurdler Edwin Moses. To my consternation, what's good for a hurdler isn't necessarily good for a long-distance runner. Training manuals suggest that shorter strides at a faster turnover are more efficient at covering ground than a loping gait. This would explain why men and women several inches shorter than me overtake me all the time—as well as the fact that they're forty to fifty pounds lighter, and therefore have that much less weight to lug around the course.

That said, even a certain stoutness isn't necessarily the burden you might think it should be. It's generally true that carrying fewer spare tires around your middle makes long-distance running easier. However, being lighter is not always better. First of all, because muscle weighs more than fat, running isn't guaranteed to make you lose the pounds. What'll happen in the course of your training is that fat will be converted into muscle, and you'll *look* thinner, especially around the waist. You'll also be stronger. Secondly, some people are blessed with incredible core strength that allows them to carry their extra bulk.

I vividly recall in one New York City Marathon being overtaken by a young man on the Queensboro Bridge who must have been six-foot-four and have weighed 250 lbs. My mother (God bless her) told me after the race that she'd noticed him powering ahead of me as well, and had been surprised that he could run so effectively. Sure, he carried a bit of excess flesh on him, but he also had enormous thighs that he was using to propel him forward.

The moral is that you've no excuse *not* to get out and run. Whether you're tall or short or carrying a little extra around the center, you'll see other runners just like you ripping past those you once thought were the "ideal" shape.   —*M.R.*

Women Shouldn't Run

"In a country where only men are encouraged,
one must be one's own inspiration."

—**Tegla Loroupe**, Kenyan distance runner,
winner of the New York City Marathon

Growing up in Hawaii in the days before TV and computers, I remember playing outdoors for hours and, living by the beach, learning to swim around the age of three or four. We had recess at elementary school where we could play on the swings and monkey bars and do a lot of running. In middle and high school, there were gym classes, and I recall participating in whatever activity was programmed for us. I enjoyed softball, basketball, volleyball, gymnastics, field hockey, swimming, and, in fact, was the only girl on the swim team. This was primarily because by this time I was going to school in Northern California, and swimming wasn't nearly as common, nor were there many girls who swam well. And if it was unusual for a girl to be on the swim team, well . . . running and track was not even conceived of for us girls in high school back in the early 1950s. I think remnants of that thinking persist to this day.

Other than that foray into swimming, I was no different from all the other girls in junior and high school in that whenever we didn't feel like doing anything, we used the excuse of having our period—frequently! I have to chuckle when I think that our gym teachers must've been on to us, but it sure worked. (For the life of me, I can't figure out why the prevailing wisdom of the time was that girls shouldn't exercise at that time of the month.) By the time I started college, however, exercise became a luxury. I had absolutely no parental support (in fact, my mother thought that college was totally wasted on girls) and, despite receiving a scholarship, I still had to work full-time to support myself. I did do a lot of walking, however, since neither my classmates nor I owned a car.

The years that followed entailed no exercise at all. I got married and soon had two children. To get back into shape after my first pregnancy I did daily sit-ups and found they were very effective; breast-feeding quickly got my weight back down to normal. During my second pregnancy, I decided to be proactive. I continued with the sit-ups, thinking that they'd prevent my poor abs from losing all of their tone. I told my obstetrician what I was doing and asked him if it could possibly harm the baby. His answer? "No, but it won't do any good, either!"

Given what I'd experienced with my first pregnancy I was sure this regimen would work, so I kept on with my daily routine, even doing twenty sit-ups the night before giving birth. And it worked! The nurses were so amazed at my flat tummy so soon after delivering my son that they called in others to take a look. This was the beginning of my learning how to take care of my muscles and maintaining a modicum of fitness.

Back in 1968, when I read *Aerobics* and learned of its many benefits, it was an "Aha!" moment for me. Instead of just exercising one part of my body—my abs—I'd exercise my entire body by running. I would become a runner, even though at that time I had never met nor heard of a woman who ran.

My First Race—My First Gold Medal

After following this routine of early morning runs for a few years, I started talking about running, telling people about "aerobics" and all its benefits. As a result, I soon became known among my friends and coworkers as "the runner." One day in 1973, several coworkers showed me a flyer announcing a 10K race on the Air Force base where I worked. They said, "You ought to enter this." *A race?* I thought. *Why not? It might even be fun.* So I signed up for it, and my morning runs took on more purpose and urgency.

As I toed the starting line on race-day morning, I looked around nervously and saw that I was the only woman. All of a sudden, I became *really* nervous. *What if I can't keep up with everyone?* I thought. *What if I finish last? Worse, what if I can't even finish? What will all these guys think?* I felt that if I didn't do well, I'd be embarrassed, laughed at, and, worst of all, I'd have let all womanhood down. I wondered why I had put myself in this position and even considered quietly slipping away and forgetting the whole thing. But, right then, the gun went off and everybody took off, nearly leaving me behind. I started running with my heart beating so hard that I thought, *What if I have a heart attack?* My next thought was, *Don't be silly, just get running.*

After the first few minutes of running, I realized that my pace was much faster than the pace of my usual morning runs and that I'd better slow down. I then focused on my own running and tried not to notice all the faster guys passing me. *Slow and steady, slow and steady*—that became my mantra—*slow and steady. Just keep going until you reach the finish line.*

I don't remember much more of that race until the finish line came into view. With a renewed burst of energy, I picked up the pace and crossed it with arms raised high and the biggest grin on my face. I did it! And, looking around, I wasn't last, either.

Shortly after, the award ceremony began and I stood there nervously wondering what was going to happen next. Then I heard my name being called. I ran up to the podium and collected my first gold medal. From then on, I was hooked. I started looking around for other races, and thus began my racing career. I remained the only woman in races for quite a while because of the idea that women shouldn't run.

Benefits for Women from Running

Actually, back in 1973 there was ostensibly *some* medical "evidence" to support the contention that women shouldn't run. At least one medical doctor claimed that women should never run because their uterus would drop and could even prolapse completely. Fortunately, I haven't heard this myth for a while, but I recall reading it when it was published as a "fact" by a physician in the early days of the running boom. While it's true that abdominal organs can prolapse, I contend that it's from exactly the opposite cause—*lack* of exercise.

The purpose of the abdominal muscles is to act as support for all the internal organs. If those muscles are kept strong, the organs stay where they belong. One set of those muscles, too often ignored, are the PCGs (the pubococcygei), which control the floor of the perineum, or pelvic floor. They also surround the urethra, which keeps urine in your bladder and prevents leakage. It's important to keep these muscles strong, not only for the job of holding organs in place but to prevent urinary and even fecal incontinence. I can cite one nursing home supervisor who said that every one of the home's occupants who has to wear adult diapers does so because he or she hasn't exercised enough. Strong PCGs are also said to enhance the quality of orgasms.

The easiest way to identify and isolate the PCG muscles is to stop the flow of urine mid-stream. Contract these muscles ten times to comprise one set, and do three sets daily to keep these muscles sturdy. Since none of us ever want any type of incontinence, men as well as women benefit from doing these exercises. You can do them any time, any place—sitting in meetings or waiting at a red light—and no one will ever know!

Other reasons cited for why women shouldn't run is that they'd grow hairy chests and mustaches, get muscular legs, and sweat. Hey, we all sweat! I guess back in the days when women tried to live up to impossible ideals of femininity, daintiness, and sweetness—and wouldn't be caught dead in running shoes—it was hard to imagine doing the grunt work of pushing oneself up a hill. And, heaven forbid, what if you were to develop muscles?

Thank goodness, a lot has changed regarding the feminine ideal—and this is true of running marathons. In fact, did you know there was a time when women weren't even *allowed* to run in marathons? (In Saudi Arabia they still aren't, the last time I checked.) I have an indelible picture in my mind of the 1967 Boston Marathon's race director trying to tear off Kathrine Switzer's race number when he discovered that the "K. Switzer" who'd entered the race was, in fact, a woman. Thankfully, Kathrine finished and instantly became a role model for female runners. So, it's only been within the last few decades that fitness for women has become fashionable and the fear of sweating and developing muscles has turned into a desire to have a lean, trim, and, yes, a muscular body. We now know that perspiring is healthy, and the primary criterion of effective exercise. While a lot more women are running than when I first started back in 1968, I'd love to see all girls and women take advantage of its many benefits. At the starting lines of races these days I see a good representation of females of all ages, so there's been a lot of progress.

There are two major benefits of running that aren't appreciated enough and certainly not promoted by medical doctors, both general practitioners as well as gynecologists. For many women and girls, regular running will help them avoid or reverse the symptoms of PMS (which I define as both Pre-Menstrual Syndrome and Post-Menopausal Syndrome). For those fighting obesity, running is a more efficient and effective way to burn calories than almost any other form of exercise—apart, perhaps, from cross-country skiing.

Women and medical knowledge have come so far that not even pregnancy interferes with running. Women are now told that if they were regular runners before they got pregnant and got the okay from their obstetrician, they can keep on running, right through their pregnancy. Look at the British marathoner and world-record-holder Paula Radcliffe, who trained through her pregnancy, scaling back to a measly every-other-day schedule during her ninth month! As far as the impact of being pregnant and becoming a mother, Paula won the New York City Marathon ten months after giving birth.

In another case of successful pregnant runners, Ingrid Kristiansen, the famous Norwegian distance runner, ran competitively during the first five months of her pregnancy, not even knowing she was pregnant. She went on to win the 1983 Houston Marathon just five months after giving birth. We now know that being pregnant is not a handicap, and that regular aerobic exercise is good for not just the mother but also the baby.

A Woman's Sport

Ruth is a genuine pioneer of running—an early adopter in the manner of Kathrine Switzer, Nina Kuscsik, Grete Waitz, Joan Benoit Samuelson, and Gloria Averbuch, who in the 1960s and 1970s were instrumental in expanding the number of women in road running and other sports leading up to and in the wake of the passage of the Patsy T. Mink Equal Opportunity in Education Act in 1972. (More commonly known as Title IX, the act banned discrimination against anyone on the basis of sex from engaging in any educational activity. The result was an explosion of girls taking part in sports in schools and colleges.)

As Ruth writes, it's hard to believe today how medieval the thinking of many athletic associations and the medical profession was regarding women's health—that women couldn't run distances beyond 1500 meters without causing themselves physical harm. Women weren't officially permitted to enter marathons until 1970 (although, as we've seen, they'd sometimes sneak into races to record unofficial times). It took another decade for women's races longer than 1500 meters to be staged at the Olympics, and the first women's Olympic marathon wasn't run until 1984.

The 1970 New York City Marathon featured one woman,

although she dropped out after fifteen miles, in part over-whelmed by the pressure she felt as the sole female to do well. In 1972, race organizers told the six women who entered the race that they'd have to set off ten minutes before the men so they didn't get in their way. When they were called to the starting line, the six promptly staged a sit-down pro-test until they were allowed to begin at the same time as the men. (These days, the elite women commence the New York City Marathon half an hour before the elite men and sub-elite men and women, so that television can cover their race without the men getting in the way!) By the end of the 1970s, women were full participants in marathons through-out America.

In recent years, women have not only become equal part-ners in running races, but in some cases outnumber the men. In October 2012, *The Baltimore Sun* reported that "of the 28,522 participants signed up for the Baltimore Running Fes-tival's four prime races on Saturday, 61 percent are women, up from 44 percent in 2003. Women now outnumber men in the marathon (62 to 38 percent), half-marathon (59–41), 5K (65–35) and relay (62–38)."[4] The 2013 Disney Marathon had more women entrants than men, and there are now several marathons and half-marathons for women only.

Gender stereotypes, of course, still exist—particularly over a perceived lack of competitiveness among ordinary female runners. Gina Kolata, writing in *The New York Times*, quotes the president of New York Road Runners, Mary Wittenberg, herself once an elite athlete: "[Women] are too inhibited to put their full passion out there. . . . They are almost afraid to be serious about a sport. They think that if they're not the best, they shouldn't care so much."[5] We men, it seems, have no such trouble proclaiming our own extraordinariness, or caring so much.

Of course, since a goodly portion of my races—whether

5Ks or full marathons—consist of my being overtaken by women both young and old, I'm a long way from being able to prove how much better I am than women. Nor should the more macho of our sex hope that ultras are a refuge from the vast numbers of women taking over a sport that used to be the pursuit of lonely male mavericks. While elite women may lag ten or so minutes behind the men in world-record marathon times, women are not only matching men stride for stride in some of the most punishing races on the planet, but are beating them with some regularity. If you don't believe me, then I'd suggest you look up the names of Pam Reed, Ann Trason, and Jenn Shelton. These women have torn up the record books and redefined not only what it means to be a successful female runner, but what it means to be a champion athlete . . . of either sex.   *—M.R.*

It's Too Hard to Start Running

"The ugliest four-letter word in the American
language is 'quit.' Don't quit."
—**Kenneth Cooper**, M.D.

t's only hard to start running if you quit for too long. I really believe that running is one of the most natural human activities. Just look at toddlers. As soon as they get the walking part sorted out, they run everywhere! Watch children at recess in nursery school, day care centers, and elementary schools. They're always running— except when teachers shout at them to stop. Back in high school, I got a job as a lifeguard at our local swimming pool. The most common part of my day was not saving people from drowning; it was blowing my whistle at kids and yelling, "Stop running!"

Sadly, after so many years of being told not to run, we let the message "take" and, as a result, a large percentage of our population *can't* run anymore. It's a perfect example of law named after the German anatomist and surgeon Julius Wolff (1836–1902): *Use it or lose it.* The ideal time to start building your fitness base is in your twenties, when you haven't lost your aerobic capacity, muscle, and bone. Yet, as noted earlier, only eleven percent of the age-group 85+ gets regular exercise. Almost everybody takes their leg muscles for granted until they find that they can't get out of a chair without help. Know that as you age, you lose about a pound of muscle a year—which may not sound like much, but over the course of ten or twenty years it really adds up.

How to Get Started

Getting started running is simple. Lean forward, put a foot out to keep yourself from falling to the ground, and keep repeating. We all started running soon after learning to walk and, for most people, that's all there is to it—assuming, of course, you have normal body architecture and are in reasonably good health. It's here that I need a CYA statement, (in common parlance, to cover my butt to keep me from being sued): *Check with your doctor before starting this or any other exercise program.* It's also beneficial to find a running group. But I do think it's wise to have a good base of running under your belt before joining a group, somewhere in the region of twenty miles a week. That said, the basics are simple: get up, get dressed, get out the door, run your chosen distance, and, hopefully, you'll end up where you want to be.

After doing this for a while, if you're like me you'll want to increase your mileage a little bit, as in "Just one more block and *then* I'll turn around." You might start out running for ten minutes, then as your body adapts, slowly increase a minute at a time until you get to twenty, then increase two minutes at a time when you feel ready to get to thirty, and so on. I hate to tell you this, but the (il)logical extension of this is a 24-hour race, or even the 48-hour races run by the Tarahumara of the Copper Canyons in Mexico (about which we'll hear more later)! Yes, there are even 100-mile races, although the closest I got to that was the 14+ hours in my first Ironman Triathlon and, once, a 24-hour relay. But I'm getting ahead of myself—and you!

All you need in the way of equipment is running shoes, socks, shorts or pants, and a running top or a singlet, sometimes optional for men. For women, there are bras made specifically for running, either sports bras or regular bras without elastic straps. I also recommend a sweatband to keep perspiration from running into your eyes, a pair of sunglasses to protect your eyes from the sun or the rain and wind, and possibly, a visor to keep the sun off your face. Sunblock or sunscreen and a hat may also be advisable.

Those are the basics. I would add a watch for keeping track of your time out running. The watch is helpful, especially when you need to follow by how much you increase your running, so you don't do too much too soon. The simple rule is to add no more than ten percent to your mileage per week, although that rule falls apart at both extremes of the running continuum. Start out comfortably, and run consistently with a running base of one to four miles before increasing. At the other end, if you're training for the Boston Marathon, for example, a five percent or lower increase may be more appropriate for your mileage level.

If you're just getting started, visit a store that sells running shoes. You'll find the best advice there because most of the salespeople are runners themselves. It can be helpful to bring with you a well-worn pair of shoes so that your "wear patterns" can be identified. Once you've put on a pair that feels really comfortable, go for a trial run to see how they feel. Most stores will let you take a short run up and down the block. Keep in mind that there's no break-in period for running shoes; they need to feel comfortable, right from the very beginning. As you get more into running, I recommend purchasing at least one additional pair so you can alternate the wearing of your shoes. It's better for both your feet and for the shoes. You might even consider giving "barefoot runners" a try. (More on this later.)

As for the selection of socks, I've tried them all! Some thick and heavy, some thin and light, and I've found that you just have to see what works best for the shoes you have. I do recommend wearing socks, because they reduce the possibility of blisters and help keep shoes relatively stink-free.

Most running shorts and pants are loose-fitting and comfortable and shouldn't cause any chafing. The same is true of tops and singlets. Get them bright-colored so that you can be seen as you run, especially if you run on roads with traffic. Traffic doesn't mean just cars, since skateboarders, cyclists, and even other runners can be hazardous. If you have to run in the dark, be sure to put some reflective tape on your clothes and shoes so drivers and everybody else can see you. Always run facing the traffic and keep an eye out for drivers who may not be paying attention. As I've found twice to my great cost, I guarantee that you'll lose in any confrontation with a ton of steel!

An accessory I've used for years is a heart-rate monitor. It's useful during your run and for checking your rate of recovery when you're at rest, either after your run or the next morning after a full night's sleep. The monitor is also a useful and fun way to tell how well your body is adapting to your training. The number of beats per minute (BPM) is an excellent gauge of how hard your heart has to work to supply the increased oxygen needs for your muscles. The average resting BPM is seventy-two. The lower you go from that baseline is generally a good guide to your fitness level. Supremely fit athletes have resting heart rates in the thirties.

Start by measuring your waking, resting heart rate. Use your heart-rate monitor or, if you don't have one, put a watch or clock with a second hand by your bedside. As soon as you awaken and before you get up, measure your BPM. You don't even have to count for a full minute, as you can count for thirty seconds and double your result, or even fifteen seconds and multiply by four. Do this frequently enough—for example, five mornings in a row—so that you know what your average range is. Then, as you increase your mileage or test yourself in a race, you can monitor your body's ability to recover. If the next morning your resting heart rate is right around that average, you'll know you have fully recovered. If, however, it's higher than average, you'll know you need to take it easy until your heart rate gets back to your normal average.

It's a lot of fun to watch the correlation between your level of effort and how your heart responds to it. I've used this to push myself to work harder at running up hills or in races. Keep in mind, though, that if you're pushing yourself so hard that something hurts you need to back off, regardless of your heart rate. Pain is your body's alarm system, akin to the red line on a car's tachometer or a warning light on the dashboard. Ignoring the alarm is like disconnecting the tachometer cable or unscrewing the red warning light—not a smart thing to do! Pay attention to what your body is telling you. You need to build up your mileage slowly to allow your body to adapt.

Once you're properly outfitted and equipped, don your new gear and head out the door. Note the time and warm up by doing a few minutes of fast walking. (I don't recommend stretching cold muscles. Do any stretching at the end of your run when your muscles are warm if you want to add stretching to your routine.) After you're feeling warmed up, break into a gentle run, paying attention to how every body part is feeling. Gradually increase your speed, again noting how your body is reacting.

With properly fitted gear, the first thing you might notice is that your breathing has increased in both rate and depth. Your muscles are requiring more oxygen, and as long as you can theoretically talk while running—the test for staying aerobic—you're getting enough oxygen. It's difficult to advise how long and how fast your first runs should be because everyone starts out at a different fitness level. Keep in mind that the most common running error is going too far, too fast, and/or too soon. So whether it's been ten minutes or four blocks, if some body part is telling you to quit or is not happy, stop for the day.

Start a journal and record your time, distance, how you felt, and anything noteworthy—such as extreme temperature, high winds, etc. As for how often to run, you might have been advised that you should run only three to four times a week. I started with daily running because I enjoyed it and didn't know any better. My advice is to establish a firm running pattern and alternate hard and easy days. For example, if you've run four blocks for your first run, you might do a bit less, perhaps three, the next day. If you're feeling good the third day, bump it up to five blocks, and so on. The time-honored rule is to increase by no more than increments of ten percent per week or month, as mentioned earlier. This is where you really need to monitor your body's reaction to the new routine. At the first sign of any ache or pain, back off until it's gone.

You can also add other exercises to your routine. I think it's important to keep your core muscles strong, so I do abdominal contractions several times a day where I just pull in my stomach hard and hold it for about thirty seconds. I do sit-ups and plank poses as part of my three-times-a-week sessions of lifting weights. The plank is getting into a push-up position, supporting yourself with just your hands and feet, and holding that position for about thirty seconds, increasing the time as you get stronger. Keep your back straight and abs contracted. This exercise is also good for your lower back and may keep you from ever having backaches, an all-too-common affliction among those of us who sit far too much.

To maintain or increase your fitness level, develop back-up alternatives such as swimming, cycling, and weightlifting. This is especially important for times when running is impossible due to injuries, traveling, or emergencies. Better yet, use this cross-training as a supplement to your weekly fitness regimen and really see gains in your fitness levels.

A Bit about Running Form

As mentioned before, running comes naturally. Because we've gotten away from running, however, we've lost the feel of effortlessly "floating" through the air and we may find that we don't know what to do with our hands, arms, hips, legs, and feet.

Generally, your hands should be open and relaxed, and your arms should swing like a pendulum forward and back, not across the front of your body. They should be bent at the elbow at approximately a ninety-degree angle. Hips should be loose enough to rotate slightly with each stride. Legs, too, should swing like a pendulum and strike the ground directly below your knees—no reaching out beyond the knee level. Your feet should land gently on their balls, pointing straight ahead, and as you complete the stride, push off as if you were pawing or doing a little swipe back. Your head should be upright, with eyes focused about six to eight feet in front of you. Not only is this a relaxed head position, it's useful for avoiding hazards such as cracks in sidewalks in urban areas and roots when running on trails that could trip you up. Ideally, you should consult someone knowledgeable, such as a trainer or coach, who can analyze your form and make any needed corrections.

Running Etiquette

If you're lucky enough to have a track to run on, this can be a great advantage. Not only can you easily measure the distance you've run, but you can also time yourself. Most tracks are 400 meters in length; therefore, four times around the track is a mile. Here are some tips to remember about track etiquette:

- Always run on the outer lanes, unless you're such a super-fast runner that no one is going to pass you. If you do run on one of the inside lanes and you hear someone behind you say "Track," immediately move to an outer lane.
- When slowing or stopping, check behind you and then move to the outside lane so you don't get mowed down or impede someone's progress.
- On bike paths or trails, stick to the right to give cyclists room to pass you.
- When running in groups on streets, run single-file, always facing traffic.
- When running with a dog, have a leash no longer than five or six feet. Make sure the dog is always under control and can't lunge at other runners.
- When running with a stroller, give way to other runners, maintaining ten to fifteen feet of clearance to prevent collisions and to protect the baby, you, and other runners.
- No spitting, please! I don't see this as often as I used to but it's

very disconcerting if you happen to be right behind someone who loves to clear his phlegm, as I was once during a race.

Dealing with the "Trots"

Bowel issues before a run or a race seem to crop up at least once in every runner's life. One of the most appreciated benefits of my diet, which I'll tell you more about in chapter five, is that I'm "regular." I recommend a high-fiber diet to handle these pre-run issues. I know that some recommend you eat a low-fiber diet the day before a race so you won't be as likely to have to use the bathroom in the morning. I think you're far better off with a good cleaning out first thing in the morning before the race, and a good, high-fiber diet will do just that.

In some cases, however, just plain old anxiety—pre-race jitters—will force a bathroom break. Fortunately, it tends to be self-limiting for most of us. When you get to be an "old hand" at this business of racing, eagerness replaces the anxiety. Most runners recognize that exercise is good for "intestinal motility," so scouting out bathrooms and bushes might be a good idea—just in case.

Barefoot Running

I mentioned "barefoot runners" earlier and you may already be familiar with the concept of "barefoot running," which may or may not be taken literally. However, in this case I'm referring to the practice of running using minimalist shoes named "barefoot runners." These shoes have very thin, light soles with no heel at all, no arches, no side supports, and allow the toes to spread out naturally. The barest of barefoot runners are a simple sole, with twine that attaches it to your foot. They're surprisingly comfortable when properly fitted. Obviously, sometimes our feet need protection from a running surface such as gravel, rocks, broken glass, or surfaces hot enough to burn your feet. But you certainly don't need a thick "mattress" to do that, either.

Proponents of barefoot runners say that the typical running shoe insulates the soles of your feet from the "feel" of the ground and prevents the twenty muscles of the foot from being properly exercised. As for arch supports, the advocates argue that sticking a support up the middle of an arch is the fastest way to break it down, just like in buildings.

I remember back in the 1980s when Jayhawks first came out. They were a model of running shoe that were, in a way, a precursor to barefoot runners. I loved them for their lighter weight, the feeling of freedom my feet experienced, and best of all, seemingly faster times. To make them last, I wore them only for races, because the company quit manufacturing them after a couple of years. They felt very close to today's barefoot runners.

There are arguments pro and con for this kind of running shoe. Bear in mind that not all agree that this is the best way to run. A podiatrist I spoke with said that she sees a rash of injured runners every ten years or so when barefoot running is "rediscovered." But if you try it, you might like it. Just be sure to do it gradually to enable your feet to adapt.[6]

100Up and 100Back

Most of my running is done in urban areas, which means a lot of stops and starts at intersections. It was totally frustrating until a dedicated runner called Randy Kreill told me of a technique he called 100Up. (You can read Randy's story in the Appendix.)

Here's a 100Up. When you reach a red light or have to stop for any reason at all, raise each knee up and count each lift until the light turns green or you can start running again. You also exercise your brain this way because you have to remember where you left off counting when you reach the next top. I frequently get up to 100, pat myself on the back for getting the extra exercise, and start the count all over again.

One day, while I was out running and was stopped at a red light, I devised a variation of the 100Up and called it the 100Back. *Because the 100Up works the quadricep muscles in the front of the thigh,* I thought, *why not strengthen the hamstrings in back as well?* So, by reversing the action and raising your heel to your backside, alternating legs, you're now working the hamstring to give them equal time. I usually do a stretch of 100Ups and then switch to 100Backs.

Running vs. Walking

The argument that walking is just as good as running for optimal health has been used by many as an excuse not to run because, as the reasoning goes, *Why bother if you burn as many calories just walking a mile as you do running a mile?* Theoretically, if you move a mass from Point A to Point B, it should take the same amount of energy in calories regardless of how fast that mass moves. People might intuitively think that this would apply to human bodies as well. As a result of this argument, there's a common belief that walking a mile will burn as many calories as running the same distance. Most people usually recognize that running does burn more calories, but they maintain that you're walking longer to complete that mile and that burns an equal amount of calories.

Researchers at Syracuse University, Department of Exercise Science, set out to see if this was true.[7] They took twelve men and twelve women and asked them to alternate running a mile and walking a mile. They even had them do the same on both a track and a treadmill. Their measurements averaged as follows:

	RUNNING	WALKING
Men	124 calories	88 calories
Women	105 calories	74 calories

The difference is actually larger when you subtract resting basal metabolic rates:

	RUNNING	WALKING
Men (net)	105 calories	52 calories
Women (net)	91 calories	43 calories

These charts show that you are in effect burning more than twice as many calories when running than when you're walking. Hopefully, this research should settle the argument, although the waters can get muddied when the walkers start walking fast enough to approach a running speed and begin to close in on the number of calories burned by the runners.

Of course, walking has its place. It's an excellent precursor to running and most people, regardless of fitness levels, can start with walking. When fitness levels increase to the point that they plateau, then running is the next logical step. At this point, running is easy!

Screwing Up

We all make mistakes—even when we think we know it all. In 2012, I finished the Brooklyn Marathon in 3:30:37. I was happy with my time, but I couldn't work out how I'd let those thirty-seven seconds get away from me. A helpful friend pointed out that twice on the course I'd stopped to re-tie my shoelaces. "That must have lasted a good fifteen seconds each time," said my supportive pal. I slapped my hand to my forehead: it was a basic error, a rookie blunder. And yet, there I was, on my thirteenth marathon, and I'd forgotten to double- or triple-tie my laces before the race.

When I decided to run my first marathon, I made three elementary mistakes that set back my training. First of all, I ran in an old pair of shoes, which landed me (in combination with the other two clangers I'll get to) with plantar fasciitis, an extremely common and annoying condition that affects the heel. As Ruth says in this chapter, shoes—or at least certain kinds of shoes—are controversial items for runners these days. I can see how "barefoot runners" might provide you with greater flexibility for trail running, but since I pound the concrete and asphalt of New York City's streets and parks, I want as much cushioning as I can get as well as protection from glass, rubble, and other things I'd rather not have on the lightly covered soles of my feet.

It's very easy to be intimidated by so-called experts who promise you all sorts of magical abilities if you just get the right gear. Read any running magazine or go to any expo before a big-city marathon and you'll see booth after booth selling all sorts of wondrous widgets and gizmos to make your race experience as smooth as possible. If you're like me, you'll get nervous, freak out, and think that, unless you purchase the newest super-duper product, you'll fall apart at mile twenty-one. Try to resist the siren song of commercialism: run what you're comfortable in and don't over-technologize something that should, as Ruth makes clear, come naturally. If you've followed your training regimen and you stick to your race plan, you'll do just fine, no matter which watch is on your wrist or what, if anything, is on your feet.

One piece of advice I would give, however, is to protect your privates! It's a truth universally acknowledged among runners that any distance over thirteen miles (give or take a few kilometers) is going to require you paying attention to bodily fluids. Unless you've prepared beforehand, you're likely to need to find a bathroom at some point; you're likely to chafe around tender areas of your body; and you're going to have to deal with hydration and/or the lack of it (depending, of course, on how hot the day is).

Plenty of resources online and in books will help you deal

with these unpleasant realities, but one observation is worth making: avoid the cotton shirt. Cotton is a wonderful, lightweight fabric. However, it's not optimal for wicking away sweat from the body. If you run in a cotton shirt over a longish distance, you'll find yourself carrying a lot of moisture and the shirt will rub against your body in a way that will cause you agony when you climb into the shower after the race. A technical shirt (don't worry, you'll get loads of them if you run a number of longer races) will remove the sweat efficiently from your body and be less likely to chafe.

The other piece of advice: Before attempting a long run, men should rub some Vaseline on their nipples and in their genital area; women should rub it beneath their armpits (around the bra) and around their groin as well. Sweat accumulating in these areas will cause soreness and chafing. Believe me, you don't want to experience the pain and discomfort when hot water hits those parts later.

The second mistake I made back in the day was that I failed to heed Ruth's advice: I did too much too fast. Numerous programs exist on the Internet to enable you to reach whatever goal you wish, and all of them tell you to start *slowly* and increase *slowly*. Your body needs time to build up its strength and awaken those muscles that have lain dormant for all those years. Don't push it too hard, too soon. Otherwise, you'll end up injured, frustrated, and feeling sorry for yourself!

The third mistake I made was not to stretch. Some trainers advocate stretching *before* a race, and this is sound advice when you're sprinting a short distance or it's cold out and your muscles need a work-over to get them functioning. Otherwise, on days when you can't see your breath and you're running a distance longer than a few miles, you don't have to warm up—running will do that for you anyway. But you absolutely should stretch *after* the race. Your muscles need time to cool down in a way that relaxes them and keeps them loose and flexible. Stretching your hamstrings, quads, calves, and Achilles' heel area following a race will help lessen the chance of injury. If you don't do it, you may end up having to wear an orthotic as I did and stop racing for weeks until the injury has healed.

Since I've been stretching after races, wearing good shoes, and not overtraining, I've been fortunate enough not to be injured. Especially after long runs, I make sure to use a foam roller on my iliotibial band (ITB)—the complex of muscle that reaches down the outside of the leg from the hip to the knee. It's my completely unscientific contention that quite a bit of hip and knee pain caused by running is because the ITB is knotted and "tight." (Many videos online can show you how to stretch and take care of your ITB and other muscle groups.)

Of course, as Ruth's running career has shown, some injuries (such as being hit by a truck) can't be foreseen. And it's always important not to try to push your way through an injury out of some misplaced belief in your own healing powers. But, in general, running should be a way to gain fitness and wellbeing and not a cause of injury and distress. Make it that way!   —M.R.

You Need to be Young, Thin, and Have the Right Genes to Run

"Genes may not be particularly important beyond the environmental characteristics that Kenyans grow up in, where they're running miles to school at an early age; it's ingrained in their culture."

—**Stephen Roth**, PH.D., Director of the Functional Genomics Laboratory, University of Maryland

Real runners come in all shapes, sizes, ages, and every other variable you can think of. But the stereotype of a "real" runner is one who looks like the Kenyans whom I mentioned in an earlier chapter. I got a taste of typecasting the other day when I went into a running shoe store to buy a pair of "barefoot runners."

As I entered the store, the twenty-something salesman inquired whether he could help me. I asked if they had gotten any of those new "barefoot" shoes in yet. He took me over to the table where they were displayed, and to my total shock and chagrin said, "These are for running, you know, not walking." It took all the control I could muster to keep from launching into my forty-plus years of running history, my sixty-plus completed marathons, and even six Ironman Triathlons! I then realized that he probably had never even seen a seventy-something female runner in his life and so assumed they didn't exist. I just smiled and said, "Yes, I *do* know!"

After my purchase of the barefoot runners, I hope he now knows better: that not all of us runners look like long, lean Kenyan runners!

But, perhaps you *would* like to look like one or at least be as healthy as one.

Longevity

Perhaps the greatest benefit of running to your health is longevity. Research shows that running on a regular basis could add six years to your life. In a press release from the European Society of Cardiology, the long-term Copenhagen City Heart Study proclaimed that "regular jogging increases longevity." The study compared the death rates of 20,000 runners and non-runners, aged twenty to ninety-three, beginning in 1976. Of these, there were a total of 1,878 runners—1,116 males and 762 females—who recorded their running routines, including how fast and for how long they ran weekly.

In the follow-up period of up to thirty-five years, 10,158 of the non-runners died while only 122 of the runners passed away. This was an *amazing* forty-four percent drop in the risk of death for both male and female runners. Breaking it out by gender, male runners can potentially extend their lives by 6.2 years and female runners by 5.6 years. And it didn't have to be slogging away for hours or at breakneck speeds, either. The most significant benefits were found at a mere 1–2½ hours weekly at a slow pace. Even elderly people can add years to their lives, as attested to by Dr. Peter Schnohr of the Copenhagen City Heart Study: "A 70-year-old will benefit and I think the benefit may be even greater for older people."[8]

The study also found other health benefits contributing to increased longevity, including improvements in oxygen uptake, insulin sensitivity, increased HDL (good) cholesterol, lower triglycerides, heart function, greater bone density, improved immune function, lowered blood pressure, reduced chance of platelet aggregation (forming blood clots), prevention of obesity, and a better psychological profile—twelve powerful health benefits easily attainable by any of us.[9] These findings are extremely important to the health of all populations, especially as health care costs (or, what we should really call it, *disease* care costs) escalate all over the world. It's sad that more countries aren't doing studies like this, because the potential gains in both the economies and health of their citizens are substantial.

A Healthy Heart

Heart disease is the number one killer of all Westerners. Two major factors lead to a healthy heart—diet and exercise—and I am sometimes asked which I would choose, if I had to pick only one as the most important. I'd have to say it's diet. After all, you'll recall that I was a very fit marathoner when diagnosed with cancer. Fortunately, you'll likely never be forced to choose only one. The healthiest diet has been shown by innumerable studies to be a low-fat vegan diet, which I'll talk about later.

Many studies show that aerobic exercise lowers the risk of heart disease. A good measure of fitness is how efficient your heart is in pumping blood to all parts of your body. It should also be obvious that the health of the heart depends on coronary arteries that are wide open and not clogged with cholesterol-laden plaque.

After running a whole bunch of marathons and doing my first Ironman Triathlon, I was getting ready to have breast reconstruction after doctors decided that I wasn't going to die any time soon. Part of the pre-surgical work-up was to have an EKG, an electrocardiogram. A bunch of electrodes were attached to me, and the EKG technician started the machine rolling. I watched as she looked at the machine, then looked at me, back at the machine, back to me, checked each of the electrodes, and then tapped the machine a couple of times. Looking very puzzled, she turned to me with both hands on her hips and said almost accusingly, "Are you a runner?" "Yes," I said. "Why?" She heaved a sigh of relief. "That explains it! The read-out is indicating a heart rate of forty-five beats per minute, and that's so low that I thought there had to be something wrong with the machine." I was thrilled to hear this, especially since I knew that the average BPM was seventy-two. I asked her if I could have a copy of that strip for "evidence." She laughed and said, "Absolutely!" Here was my own proof that I was on the right track for the highest levels of fitness and heart health.

What about lowering your risk of heart disease by drinking a glass of red wine, which is supposed to help thin the blood with its so-called heart-healthy resveratrol? That's another case of treating the symptom rather than getting to the cause. If you're eating a diet that does not cause the factors that lead to heart disease, then you don't need any form of alcohol or blood thinners to thin the blood. Alcohol in any dose is toxic to every cell in the body, especially the brain. You should also know that alcohol shrinks the prefrontal cortex, the "executive center," of the brain. Alcohol has no place in a healthy lifestyle, and the same should go without saying about smoking.

A Healthy Brain

What good is a strong, fit, long-living body without a healthy brain? Researchers have wondered why exercise would build brainpower in ways that just thinking or problem-solving wouldn't. The brain, like all muscles and other organs, is tissue, and its function tends to decline with age and lack of use. Beginning in our late twenties, we lose about one percent annually of the volume of our hippocampus, the key part of the brain related to memory and certain types of learning.

Exercise does, however, seem to slow or even reverse the brain's physical decay, just as it does with muscles. (Remember Wolff's Law, *Use it or lose it*.) We used to think that humans were born with a finite number of neurons (brain cells) and could never generate more. Thankfully, that's been proven wrong. Using a technique that marks newborn cells, researchers determined during autopsies of adults that the brain contained lots of new neurons, especially in the hippocampus. This indicated a process called neurogenesis, the creation of new neurons.

What was even more exciting was that exercise seemed to jump-start the neurogenesis. University of Illinois's Justin Rhodes, Ph.D., who with others has done research on running and brainpower, found that the increase in neurons only came with physical exercise.[10] More mental stimulation alone, such as doing crossword puzzles or Sudoku, did not. So, in this respect, it appears that brain fitness seems to correlate well with physical fitness. The more we run, the more endorphins we produce, which sets up a positive reinforcement loop, which makes us want to run even more. All this applies equally to children, so it behooves us to get them out running as well. My theory is that if you can keep kids running through adolescence, you'll have a lifelong runner. It seems to me that our future heavily depends on the next generation being smart as well as fit.

And, what does the brain use for fuel? Only glucose! This is another reason for a plant-based, low-fat diet, and another reason why high-protein diets are really not healthy. We need those good carbohydrates, which are the source of our glucose—fuel for the brain.

Ever Heard of "Dumb Jocks"?

You may have heard the old stereotype that runners are "jocks" and "jocks" aren't very bright. I remember back in high school, we girls thought of boys as being either "brains" or "jocks," never both. But a lot of research shows that exercise is good for the brain. A 2009 study published by the Swedish National Academy of Sciences showed that boys aged 15–18 who increased their fitness by running or skiing scored significantly higher on IQ tests than those who didn't. Maria Aberg, M.D., of the University of Gothenburg in Sweden, reviewed fitness and IQ scores for more than a million males who enlisted for mandatory military service, and "in every measure of cognitive functioning they analyzed, from verbal ability to logical thinking to geometrical perception to mechanical skill, average scores increased according to aerobic fitness."[11] Over the years I've found that the best competitive runners are also the smartest and brightest people I know!

Alzheimer's Disease

A major enigma in the medical system relates to the diagnosis, treatment, and, dare I say "cure," for Alzheimer's Disease—or any type of dementia, for that matter. As our society ages, even as our bodies continue to operate, the memory and our cognitive functions can fail with devastating results. I've seen it firsthand, but maybe not surprisingly, never in a runner. On the other hand, in those cases I have seen, they were not exercisers at all. I'm not the only one who's observed this.

Researchers at the University of Washington took 153 Alzheimer's patients and gave half of them thirty minutes of daily exercise.[12] The other patients acted as a control group, and both groups got "routine" care. After two years, the exercise group was still active, had less depression, and was in better physical shape, with fewer signs of frailty. In another study conducted at Utah State University, 400 women, aged 70–80, were followed for eighteen years.[13] Their BMI (Body Mass Index) and results of neuropsychiatric tests were followed. On average, the women who developed Alzheimer's had a BMI two to three points higher than the mentally healthy women. At age seventy, each 1.0 increase in BMI raised Alzheimer's risk by thirty-six percent. This is highly significant because of the increasingly sedentary habits and obesity in the U.S. and other Western countries (to say nothing about non-Western countries that are fast adopting our unhealthy lifestyles). It is presently estimated that 22 million people will be living with Alzheimer's by the year 2025. These numbers will be even higher given current trends toward greater numbers of obese people. Just think what a difference we could make if we could keep all those seniors running!

Strong Bones

Now, what good is a healthy heart and lots of brainpower if our bones grow so full of holes that a sneeze can break a rib or stepping off a curb can break a hip? Osteoporosis is being diagnosed so frequently now that it seems that almost every senior walking into a doctor's office walks out with a prescription for one of the so-called "bone-building" drugs. Drugs, calcium pills, and dairy products are not the answer. Actually, studies show that the countries with the highest dairy consumption have the highest rates of hip fractures.

A vegan diet and aerobic exercise—as long as the latter is some kind of weight-bearing exercise like running, jumping, or even dancing—are the answer to maintaining strong bones. Some would say that any high-impact activity is harmful to joints, but what they don't know is that any impact stimulates the osteoblasts, the bone-building cells, through a process called the *piezoelectric effect*. Kenneth Cooper, M.D., who wrote *Aerobics,* calls the process "striking" and agrees that this is what stimulates increases in bone density.[14] The striking is precisely why running is so much more effective than walking to build strong bones, because the way most people walk generally produces no impact.

Bones are hardly the dead skeletons that most people picture in their minds. According to the radiologist who was watching the "hot spots" on my bone scans right after my cancer diagnosis, bones are the most metabolically active tissues in the body. If you've ever watched a bone scan in progress, you would see what he meant. Bones are continuously remodeling and respond very well to the stresses running puts on them, as long as any increase is done gradually. Dr. Karl Insogna of the Yale School of Medicine's Bone Center comments that, "Every bit as dynamic as other tissues, bone responds to the pull of muscles and gravity, repairs itself, and constantly renews itself."[15]

Unfortunately, however, most doctors and their patients still think that the answer is in a pill and not in an effective exercise such as running, which along with a diet high in leafy greens, supply all of the minerals that make up the "construction" materials for our very dynamic bones. My osteoporosis experience verified this. At the time of my cancer diagnosis and subsequent change to a vegan diet, one of my concerns was that in giving up all dairy products my bones would fall apart. I'd been taught, as have most of us, that strong bones depend on dairy products for their calcium. I was concerned enough to get a bone-density test at the time, a baseline, so I could track what was happening to my bones.

The average female reaches peak bone density of 417 mg at around ages thirty to thirty-five and typically starts losing from then on. My first test, at age forty-eight, resulted in a score of 447 mg. Obviously, I was way above that 417 mg score and was told it was undoubtedly all that running (fifteen years of daily running at that time, including a bunch of marathons) that was responsible for those high test scores.

Of course, I was pleased at those numbers, but then I reasoned that once I hit menopause, I might really go downhill fast, since, again, that is what I'd been told would happen. In the meantime, I'd started training for the Ironman Triathlon. I took the next bone-density test a year later, and had a score of 466. The third test, another year later, scored even higher.

This *increase* contradicted everything we've been told about bone density. First, I'd been told that you need calcium pills and dairy products to build strong bones; I was consuming neither. Secondly, we're told that once we hit menopause, bone density will drop along with our estrogen levels unless we take one of the "bone-building" drugs, lots of calcium, and estrogen-replacement hormones. Again, I had none of those. I couldn't even undergo any estrogen replacement therapy because my cancer was estrogen-receptor positive. Any additional estrogen would have been akin to pouring gasoline on a fire.

With all my training and my low-fat vegan diet, my bones are obviously dense enough to handle whatever stresses and strains I put on them. It should be obvious that a vegan diet provides all the "construction" materials for good, strong bones. Sadly, I know of someone to whom the opposite happened—my own mother. She was one of those senior citizens who walked into a doctor's office and was diagnosed with osteoporosis. She was immediately put on a "bone-building" drug, plus calcium pills, and was told to increase her consumption of dairy products. I wasn't able to convince her to start running and to give up the pills and dairy products.

One day, I got a call from the hospital that my mother had fallen and had to have surgery to repair not her hip, but her femur, the strongest bone in the body. It's now been discovered that when women are on these drugs for more than five years, the femur fracture-rate increases. Once seniors are immobilized and unable to do any weight-bearing exercise, it's usually downhill from there. Unfortunately, that is exactly what happened to my mother, who sadly died soon after.

Hypertension (High Blood Pressure)

Back in 1967—my pre-running days—I was at a doctor's office for a routine visit and had my blood pressure checked. I was surprised to be told that my blood pressure was a little high, that I was pre-hypertensive. Being so young, only thirty-two, I really didn't give it much thought (you know that feeling of invulnerability that most of us have when we're young). It did bother me, but I had no idea what to do about it.

As it happened, I started daily running the following year and within just a few months, my blood pressure dropped into a nice, normal zone. Thus, I found another reason to run. I like to joke about this when talking to people: The good news? Running lowers your blood pressure. The bad news? The effect lasts for only twenty-four hours, so you have to run every day! For the past forty-five years, my blood pressure has ranged around 90/60—a very healthy reading.

Weight Control

We all know that obesity rates are sky-rocketing, along with concomitant costs and the misery that it causes for both the sufferer and the medical system trying to deal with the problem. Diet books continue to zoom to the top of best-seller lists. Supplements promising to get you bikini-ready in thirty days sell like hotcakes. TV commercials show beautiful bodies that they promise could be obtained if you just bought their products. The Food and Drug Administration announces approval of yet another weight-loss drug.

What's truly scary is that our children are getting fatter and fatter at ever younger ages—starting, in some cases, even before they're born. Being overweight drastically increases a child's risk of Type-2 Diabetes, which was once seen only in adults. In fact, it used to be called "adult onset diabetes." No more. All of us need to get more active and eat a better diet. In my experience, diet is much more relevant to maintaining a healthy weight than exercise, because I found that even during my heaviest training it seemed that it was always easier to take in more calories than I burned.

There's been some research on how exercise affects appetite and the brain, but the results aren't clear. Dr. Todd Hagobian of California Polytechnic State University says, "Exercise has a definite impact on food reward regions, but that impact depends on the individual and type of exercise."[16] He experimented with a group of young, fit people who completed prolonged, strenuous, endurance sessions and found that to achieve weight loss and weight maintenance, it was necessary to exercise, and often. In other words, to have a significant *decrease* in your desire for food, you might need to sweat for an hour and preferably already be lean and fit.

According to Dr. Hagobian, researchers four or five years ago believed there were "appetite hormones" that controlled how much and when you ate. However, he's now convinced that it's the brain that's in charge of appetite, and that the right amount and type of exercise could help change the messages coming from the brain. Being fit, he says, has psychological effects in that it encourages you to maintain healthy habits, such as a proper diet, that will contribute to weight loss.

Diabetes Prevention

We've already mentioned Type-2 Diabetes. It's a terrible affliction that can lead to blindness, kidney dialysis, gangrene, amputation of limbs, and worse. Yet it's generally very easy to reverse. Exercise has a profound effect on insulin, allowing it to escort the glucose (blood sugar) into working muscles. (Of course, the muscles have to be working for it to count.) Most people believe that diabetes is caused by eating carbohydrates and high-sugar foods, because of the high sugar levels in the blood.

What nobody tells them is that it's the typical American diet—the high-fat, high-protein diet—that blocks the blood sugar from getting into the muscles. And if people aren't exercising, the muscles aren't contracting and therefore don't need, *and can't use*, the blood sugar anyway, so the sugar just builds up in the bloodstream, with deadly consequences. The pancreas keeps pouring out insulin in an attempt to lower the blood sugar, and after a while, cells lose their sensitivity to insulin, in what we call *insulin resistance*. The end result may be that the poor pancreas just completely gives out. When the pancreas can't produce insulin, we call that Type-1 Diabetes, which can occur along with Type-2.

There's even a Type-3 Diabetes. This is thought to be a hybrid form of diabetes, and is sometimes called Brain Diabetes. The brain can also produce insulin, and when it can't produce enough, brain cells die and we suffer memory loss, along with the inability to create memories. Researchers believe the key to avoiding all three types of diabetes is to maintain a healthy weight, which comes from adequate exercise and a good diet. It's so easy to prevent, but so few are told how to do it. What's really criminal is that most cases of Type-2 Diabetes can be completely reversed by simply changing to a low-fat vegan diet and getting some daily exercise.

Varicose Veins

Earlier, I wrote that before I started running at age thirty-three, I noticed the start of varicose veins. These took the form of slightly bulging, blue veins on the backs of both my legs and small, purple, spider veins on the fronts of both my thighs. While I was very disappointed at seeing what I thought were signs of aging, I wasn't too surprised as both my mother and my aunt on my father's side had them. In fact, my aunt had to have the veins surgically stripped from her legs because they were so bad. Consequently, I'd been resigned to getting them, since women on both sides of my family had them. I assumed I'd just gotten "bad genes."

You can imagine my surprise and delight when about a year after I started running, I happened to read something about varicose veins, remembered that I'd noticed them in myself, and checked both the front and backs of my legs. To my amazement and relief, I couldn't find a single sign of either the large veins or the small spider veins. To this day, I still don't see any evidence whatsoever of varicose veins.

While this is hardly a scientific study, I'm confident that it was my running that reversed the onset of varicose veins. This is also supported by a finding noted by James Fries, M.D., from Stanford University and coauthor of a 2008 study cited in note thirty-two, who observed a lower risk of varicosities in runners. In addition to varicose veins, my back problems also disappeared when I started running.

Skin Cancer

You'd think that with all the time spent outdoors, runners are at a greater risk for skin cancer. There is some debate as to whether more or less exposure to the sun is better for your health, because we all need vitamin D, which is actually a hormone our skin produces when exposed to the sun. But because skin cancer is the most common type of cancer—and one type of it, malignant melanoma, is so deadly—the mainstream approach is to slather yourself with sunscreen or sunblock whenever you're exposed to the sun.

Then there's the other side of the argument regarding the correlation between sun exposure and cancer risk. A 2012 study of 450,000 subjects, ages 50–71, showed some unexpected results.[17] Subjects were followed for nine years and controlled for extraneous factors such as body mass, exercise level, and smoking. The study found that those who had the greatest sun exposure had the lowest risk of cancers of the lung, prostate, colon, thyroid, pancreas, and several other types.

Health and fitness expert Dr. Marc Sorenson, the author of *Solar Power for Optimal Health*, believes that sunlight and vitamin D may just save your life. He claims that if you're eating a low-fat vegan diet and getting enough sun exposure to elevate your levels of vitamin D to a satisfactory level, your risk of contracting cancer is lower—especially that most dangerous form of skin cancer, melanoma.[18] Fruits and veggies are high in antioxidants, which destroy free radicals that may lead to cancer. So I say, "Use broccoli as your sun protection!"

Effect on Hormones

The increased circulation promoted by aerobic exercise benefits the endocrine system, the source of our hormones. We already know that exercise has a profound effect on insulin, allowing it to escort the glucose into working muscles, and thus prevent diabetes. But did you know that our sex hormones benefit from frequent, vigorous exercise? In the case of testosterone, it appears to raise levels in both males and females, leading to feelings of well-being, greater strength, better performance, and faster recovery. And, if you think this might have a very positive effect on your libido, you'd be right!

Exercise seems to have the opposite effect on estrogen levels, leading to lower levels, thus accounting for the lower rates of breast cancer in active women. Running, I feel, is especially important for women because it increases intestinal motility, which in turn decreases the reabsorption of estrogen. (When you get constipated, more estrogen gets reabsorbed from the colon, increasing your risk of breast cancer.) Ghrelin is the appetite-stimulating hormone as it sends hunger signals to the brain; leptin tells you when you're full. Leptin levels correlate with metabolism and help regulate appetite; exercise helps normalize these hormones. These processes are what make weight control much easier when you get enough effective exercise.

Sailing through Menopause

Since I started running at the age of thirty-three, well before the onset of menopause, and have been running up until well past seventy-five, obviously I ran through peri-menopause as well as menopause. However, I had absolutely none of the symptoms associated with the change of life. The symptoms that typically make menopausal women miserable are hot flashes, insomnia, weight gain, fat (especially abdominal), vaginal dryness, mood swings, depression, crying jags, loss of libido, and more. All of this doesn't have to happen if you keep active and eat the right diet so you don't gain weight.

Apparently, women in non-Western cultures seem to have fewer or sometimes none of these symptoms. For example, in Japan women going through menopause don't experience hot flashes and, in fact, there isn't even a word in the Japanese language for the condition. This, however, is partly due more to Japanese women's healthier diet than their exercise regimens, although running is popular in Japan as well. The 2012 Honolulu Marathon entrants, for instance, were sixty percent Japanese—with what seemed to be to be a high percentage of women of all ages.

Vigorous exercise such as running does tend to normalize female hormones, and therefore those symptoms tend not to occur during menopause. This seems to apply to pre-menstrual syndrome (PMS) as well.

Running to Overcome Jet Lag

It's a given that exercise has many benefits to our health. Here's another one, if you do any traveling across time zones. Taking a run as soon as you reach your destination does much to help your body adjust to the new time, depending, of course, on what the local time is. If you can't run outside, a treadmill does the trick. In any case, arrival in a new location seems to me to be the best reason to leave your hotel room and run to scout out the new scenery, which is hardly ever boring.

When I was still working for the Air Force in Hawaii, I had to make a number of trips to bases in South Korea. Travel was usually by military aircraft and so we'd land, many hours later, on an airfield right on base. Although tired and jet-lagged, I knew that the best thing for me to do was to go out for a run. Sure enough, the run seemed to reset my body clock to whatever the local time was, and the recovery time was minimal. I found that I could get to work almost immediately, eat meals at the local time, and most importantly, I think, be able to get a good night's sleep. It made all the difference in accomplishing the mission of the trip.

Researchers at the University of Kentucky have conducted a study that looks at the role of exercise as a *zeitgeber*.[19] The *zeitgeber*, a German word for "time giver," is in essence a time cue: it tells your body whether it's night or day and synchronizes its internal clocks. The strongest and most familiar *zeitgeber* is light (or, specifically, light–dark cycles), but there are others, such as when it's time to eat. And, as it's been discovered, exercise.

Most of the cells in your body have circadian clock genes that make their function wax and wane within a period of about a day. The clocks aren't perfect, though, so they constantly have to be resynchronized by the central timekeeper (your hypothalamus) and by external cues such as daylight, the "blue" light of computers and other electronics, or total darkness. Researchers have found that exercise can shift circadian rhythms and thus confirm that exercise is an *independent zeitgeber*, unrelated to the light–dark cycle.

So what are the practical implications? The University of Kentucky researchers point to a 2010 experiment by a Japanese group,[20] which found that we are able to adjust to an eight-hour time change more quickly if we're exposed to exercise at the same time each day. This seems to help us settle into a new sleep–wake schedule more quickly. Interestingly, the exercise didn't seem to affect the rise and fall of melatonin levels in the blood, which is a marker of the brain's clock.

These experiments tell us that the body has several different methods of keeping time. Exercise doesn't reset all of them, but it helps with some of them, which is something to keep in mind if you're struggling with jet lag. In fact, even if you're not traveling, it's still important to keep your body clock running on a fairly regular rhythm. The researchers also point out that with increasing associations between clock disruption and metabolic disease, regularly scheduled exercise may be useful as a lifestyle treatment to synchronize rhythms in humans.

Of course, this raises lots of questions. Is there a particular time that's best for us to exercise? Does it vary for different people, since we all have slightly different circadian periods? No one knows for sure, but it seems like another good reason to get out for a run after a long trip.

Measures of Fitness

Resting heart rates are often used as a measure of athletic fitness and, as I've mentioned before, on average run around seventy-two beats per minute (BPM). We've seen that runners' BPM can get down in the thirties, and mine is forty-five BPM. Blood pressure is also a common measure of fitness, and a healthy measurement is no higher than 120/80 (some now say 115/75 is better). The first number, the systolic, is the measure of the pressure on the arteries with each heart beat; and the lower number, the diastolic, is the pressure on the arteries in between beats. After my hypertensive scare, mine has settled down to around 90/60.

A third measure of fitness is the VO_2 max, the maximum oxygen consumption level. While being treated for breast cancer, I got to know several of the doctors at the hospital very well. Because of my unique medical history, they were also interested in why a fit, seemingly healthy marathoner would contract breast cancer. I was put through a number of tests, the VO_2 max being one of them. This measures the amount of oxygen your lungs can extract from the air as you're running on a treadmill. To give you an idea of the norm for my age-group, a score of thirty-two or higher would have put me in the "excellent" category. My score was 48.2 ml/kg/min. We were all amazed to find that I scored the second highest ever recorded at the clinic, and the highest was a very fit, young medical student.

Mainstream Support

Running is not an oddball, outlier activity. Even the government supports what we're saying! To quote the Centers for Disease Control and Prevention:

> There are 1,440 minutes in every day. Schedule 30 of them for physical activity!
>
> Regular exercise is a critical part of staying healthy. People who are active live longer and feel better. Exercise can help you maintain a healthy weight. It can delay or prevent diabetes, some cancers and heart problems.[21]

Most adults need at least thirty minutes of moderate physical activity at least five days per week. Examples include walking briskly, mowing the lawn, dancing, swimming, and bicycling. Stretching and weight training can also strengthen your body and improve your fitness level. The key is to find the right exercise for you. If it's fun, you're more likely to stay motivated. You may want to walk with a friend, join a class, or plan a group bike ride. If you've been inactive for a while, use a sensible approach and start out slowly.

With all this proof that running is one of the most effective, one of the least expensive, and one of the most convenient exercises almost everyone can do, why isn't the medical profession recommending it to all their patients? Instead of writing a prescription for drugs, doctors should be writing "One hour of running daily."

One reason they don't is the persistence of the myths covered here. But I suspect the biggest reason is, as the U.S. Department of Health and Human Services reports, that "once a new piece of scientific evidence emerges as a medical advance, it takes up to *17 years* before doctors routinely incorporate that information into how they practice medicine" (italics mine).[22] This is why change has been so slow and why it may be many more years before patients will be routinely advised to start a running program and fuel it with a vegan diet.

The Age-Graded Calculator

Among the many nuggets of interesting information one can mine from Christopher McDougall's book *Born to Run* is research by Dr. Dennis Bramble. Bramble analyzed the results of the 2004 New York City Marathon and looked at the relative finishing times by age. He discovered that if you were at X level of running fitness at the age of nineteen and you trained, you'd reach your peak level of running fitness at the age of twenty-nine. That was the bad news. The good news was that, if you maintained the training that took you to that peak level of fitness (whether intense or lackadaisical) at twenty-nine, you'd return to your nineteen-year-old running fitness level at . . . *sixty-four years old.*

McDougall describes the theories as to why this might be, one of which is that, early on in our evolution, we needed to keep moving continuously to find our prey, and when we located it, we caught it by chasing after it until we exhausted it. This adaptive behavior didn't entail us sprinting from one place to the next, but required a sort of continuous running/ walking over many, many miles, harassing our prey until it no longer had the energy to avoid us.

Whether you believe this theory or not, it's striking how small is the drop-off in ability between those in their thirties, forties, fifties, and early sixties. To take a random example: the Joe Kleinerman 10K Classic, staged by New York Road Runners on January 5, 2013. Here are the times of the first-placed men and women in their respective age-groups:

AGE	MEN	WOMEN
1–19	36:49	36:43
20–24	37:34	38:40
25–29	31:34	35:59

AGE	MEN	WOMEN
30–34	31:15	38:27
35–39	35:56	39:07
40–44	35:20	41:16
45–49	36:32	38:54
50–54	39:41	42:22
55–59	38:55	43:06
60–64	41:26	53:52
65–69	44:12	59:19
70–74	46:36	56:35
75–79	55:28	1:01:19
80–99	1:24:20	1:26:44

You can see that both male and female winners in the 25–29 age-group ran faster than those in the under-twenty age-group. The difference between the male winner of the 20–24 age-group and that of the 55–59 is only 81 seconds, while the female winner in the 45–49 age-group is only 14 seconds slower than a woman a quarter of a century younger. Interestingly, the ages when women are having children and subsequent to menopause are when the times between men and women diverge most substantially. Middle-aged women runners are competitive with their male counterparts. The fact that our abilities decline so slowly over such a long span of time is wonderful news for runners who started a little later in life than others. Of course, the more you run (as Ruth so ably demonstrates) the more you hold off the inevitable.

Ripeness Is All

As you do slow down, a wonderful companion called the *age-graded calculator* can perk you up no end. If, like me, you're a competitive son of a gun, you may find yourself wondering mid-race how to estimate your fitness level, given that the race has people of all ages and both sexes running it. Well, some smart people at the World Association of Veteran Athletes gathered the world-record performances for every age at a bunch of distances for both men and women and published the tables in 1989. Since then, more records have been added, and the result is an algorithm that allows you to compare and contrast yourself with others. By tabulating your age, sex, the distance of the race, and your time, you can estimate your relative fitness levels. If your percentile is under sixty, you're an average runner (which means, of course, you're average for those who actually show up to run!). If it's under seventy, then you're locally competitive. If you land in a percentile under eighty, you've attained regional class. Between eighty and ninety, you're national class, and over ninety you can consider yourself a world-class athlete.

So, what does this look like? The winner of the 75–79 women's age-group in the Joe Kleinerman 10K Classic I analyzed above was the seventy-nine-year-old Ginette Bedard, a Canadian-born resident of Queens, New York, who only took up running at sixty-eight years of age, and has been rewriting the record books ever since. I've seen her powering around courses of different lengths in New York City on a number of occasions, at one point barely beating her to the finish line of a half-marathon. Ginette's secret to coming in first is not only (as Ruth knows well) to keep on running long after others in your age-group have packed it in, but to maintain a level of fitness that slows down your decline.

By finishing the Joe Kleinerman 10K in a time of 1:01:19, Ginette Bedard had an age-graded percentile of 87.31 percent, which makes her one of the fastest women in the nation. To be honest, this is something of a decline, given that in 2009 Ginette finished the New York City Marathon in a time of 4:09:57, which since she was a mere seventy-six years of age gave her an age-graded percentile of 101 percent. This percentile provides her with an equivalent running time for a woman at the peak of her powers of 2:12:54, a time that would beat by almost three minutes Paula Radcliffe's 2003 world record of 2:15:45 for a woman marathoner! While all the hoopla rightly surrounded the Ethiopian Derartu Tulu, who won the female division of the 2009 marathon in a time of 2:28:52, the Kenyan was *effectively* sixteen minutes *slower* than the septuagenarian from Far Rockaway.

Ginette is a remarkable athlete in that her late entry into the world of competitive running not only kept her fit, but actually made her fitter—and exponentially, almost miraculously so. In the 2003 New York City Marathon, at the age of seventy, Ginette finished first in her age-group in a time of 4:52:30—a pace of slightly more than eleven minutes per mile and with an age-graded percentile of sixty-six, a very respectable showing indeed. Ginette, however, wasn't content with simply being respectable! The following year, she finished the race almost an *hour* earlier (3:57:04), at a pace almost two minutes quicker per mile than the year before. This catapulted her to an age-graded percentile of 82.75, making her nationally competitive.

She wasn't done yet. In 2005, aged seventy-two, Ginette ran the same race over ten minutes faster still (3:46:18), for an age-graded percentile of eighty-eight, at a pace of 8:38 per mile. Age, of course, catches up with everyone eventually. But we needn't be worried about Ginette's slight drop off in form just yet. In the second half of 2013, she entered a new age bracket (80–85), which will give her an advantage over older runners and allow her to set even more records. It's a fair bet that she'll do very well in the 2013 New York City Marathon.

These are the delicious opportunities and ironies that await the runner as he or she ages—one of the several benefits that, as Ruth has shown, the mature athlete can look forward to in relation to her peers. It's also a warning to those of us who haven't traveled quite as far along the primrose path of life that, for all our bravado and zip, those riper gentlemen and ladies who surround us may, in fact, be world champions in disguise. Yes, they may cross the finish line after us and look just like any other mid-packer out for a constitutional. But the age-graded calculator shows that they were, in effect, miles and minutes ahead of us, breasting the tape and breaking records!   —*M.R.*

You Need to Change Your Diet to Run

"What makes my body run the best? The answer turned out to be simple. Plants make it run the best."
—**Rich Roll**, ultramarathoner and triathlete

*A*ctually, all you really need from your diet in order to run is calories, so you don't *need* to change your diet, but you may want to if you're not eating the best diet to support your running. There's a lot of confusion about food, nutrition, and diet out there. Just look around and you'll see that most people are not eating the healthiest of diets. Then look at the hundreds, if not thousands, of diet books available, each one purporting to be the "last word" on what we humans should be eating.

Years ago, one concept that scientists were aware of was that muscles need carbohydrates. If you were going to run something like a marathon, you'd need an awful lot of carbohydrates. In the 1960s, a Swedish physiologist named Gunvar Ahlborg discovered a positive relationship between the amount of glycogen (carbohydrates stored in the muscles and liver) in the body and endurance performance. If you deprived yourself of carbohydrates for a few days before a race, then loaded up on pasta the night before the competition, theoretically your muscles would overcompensate and take up more carbohydrates than they would normally.

This is the origin of the "carbo-loading" pasta dinners the night before a big race. If, however, you're eating a plant-based diet, you're always carbo-loading, and that's the way it should be for the most effective training. Since the 1960s, scientists have discovered that there's no need for the early-deprivation phase. The carbohydrates found in whole plant foods are the perfect fuel—not only for the race, but for all the necessary training you do beforehand, and for fueling the perfect, healthy body we all should and could have. This isn't to say you shouldn't eat a "carbo-loading" dinner the night before a race. Just make sure you're eating whole grain pasta with plain marinara sauce, and stay away from fats such as butter, most salad dressings, and most desserts for best health and race results.

The general public is so confused about carbohydrates. People don't realize that when they refer to a "low-carb" diet, they eliminate the healthiest foods of all—fruits and vegetables. Taken as a group, fruits and vegetables generally average about eighty percent of their calories from carbohydrates. Because some very popular low-carbohydrate diets were so effective in weight loss by making you sick, carbohydrates got a bad rap. These low-carb diets worked because they put the dieter into a state of ketosis, which is when the body is so low in glucose that ketones are used as fuel. When in ketosis, you frequently feel so sick that you have no appetite. Although these diets were good in that they eliminated the "white stuff"—refined, processed, white flour products—they were hardly healthy.

What I Thought I Knew about Nutrition

After completing my first college nutrition course way back in 1952, I *thought* I knew what a healthy diet was: lots of protein in the form of animal foods and lots of calcium from dairy products. The professor told us that everybody needed to drink lots of milk to have strong bones. Little did I know then that so-called "lactose intolerance" was your body's way to tell you it was time to get yourself weaned!

I followed those nutritional guidelines until my cancer diagnosis in 1982. In fact, I held on to that *Diet and Disease* textbook for years, referring to it frequently, thinking it would ensure that I was getting all the essential nutrients. That was the situation when, after just having my cancer surgery, I saw a notice in the local newspaper that read, "Wanted: Women with breast cancer to participate in diet research study." I bolted to the phone because this was exactly where I was mentally—desperate to talk to anybody who knew anything about cancer and, especially, was conducting research in that field. Both my surgeon and oncologist told me they didn't know why I had gotten breast cancer—indeed, that *nobody* knows why we get cancer. Here, I thought, was a chance to find out how this could have happened to me, especially given my background in nutrition and having been a daily runner for fourteen years. I was sure I was eating the best diet possible and, having run several marathons, I knew I was pretty fit.

The researcher conducting that study was Dr. John McDougall, who at the time was practicing medicine in Hawaii. Dr. McDougall had noticed through an analysis of Hawaii's multicultural population, that different ethnic groups and age-groups had different incidence rates for certain chronic diseases. He'd been a plantation doctor on the Big Island and had observed three generations of Japanese, Filipino, and Caucasians. The chronic diseases included heart disease, cancer, strokes, high blood pressure, diabetes, and obesity. The old Japanese and Filipino men were healthy, strong, lean, and in some cases fathering children into old age. The middle generation was less healthy. The third generation, however, was obese, diabetic, hypertensive, and, in general, not healthy at all. Dr. McDougall figured out that diet had a lot to do with the degeneration of their health and set out to prove it, starting with the clinical research study on breast cancer.

In response to the ad, I was told to gather my medical records and meet Dr. McDougall in his office the next day. As he looked over my lab tests, he frowned and said, "You know, with a cholesterol reading of 236, you're at as high a risk of dying of a heart attack as the breast cancer." I was doubly stunned! First the breast cancer, and now Dr. McDougall was saying I could die of a heart attack? He hastened to reassure me that by changing my diet I would beat both of these: "If you want to save your life, change your diet!"

Despite my having had surgery in which the surgeon attempted to cut out all the cancer, there were no clear margins. The cancer had already spread throughout the breast. There were also signs that it was in my bones, liver, and one lung as well. So I was desperately afraid it was too late. Dr. McDougall assured me that that was not the case. He said that if I enrolled in his study, I couldn't have any chemotherapy or radiation because he needed to show that it was the *diet* alone—not chemo or radiation—that reversed the cancer and saved my life. This meant that the diet would be the only variable, and therefore strong evidence that this cancer was diet-related. This was really good news to me, not only because I would have done anything to save my life, but because I'd be able to avoid chemo and radiation.

The diet I was to follow consisted of fruits, vegetables, legumes, and whole grains. I already loved brown rice and oatmeal, so that part was easy. I took Dr. McDougall's cooking class and learned how to make a wide variety of delicious foods, all based on whole plant foods, and to skip all oils, even olive oil. The basic idea was to take ethnic dishes and keep them healthy. For example, chili con carne without the meat, spaghetti without the meatballs, and stir-frys with lots of different veggies sautéed in water or veggie broth. The options are almost endless, all very healthy, but, most importantly, delicious!

The simplest and most basic eating plan I adopted, however, was to eat just whole, unrefined, unprocessed plant foods, especially many different varieties of fruit and veggies. As I like to say, "Just wash 'em and eat 'em!" There was an almost infinite variety of dishes that could be made following these simple guidelines, and thus my new diet was launched.

One relatively unique aspect of my diet was an emphasis on leafy greens, which I even included in my breakfast. While studying nutrition, I learned which foods had the highest vitamin, mineral, and antioxidant levels, and were therefore the healthiest. Leafy greens are right at the top, so it made a lot of sense to me to get them into my body as early in the day as possible—and not in the form of a small dinner salad as so many people do.

As I recovered from the cancer surgery and increased my training, I would tuck bananas, apples, orange slices, raisins, or brown rice balls into my waist pack to eat on the run or on long bike rides. I sometimes made my own healthier version of trail mix using only raisins, dates, and other dried fruit such as bananas, mangoes, and papayas. When traveling, I'd carry plain baked potatoes and eat them as you would an apple. Sweet potatoes and yams also made for good, healthy, and very portable food. Water was my only beverage and was my first choice at race aid stations.

Because I was so frequently asked about my diet—questions like "What's wrong with fish?" and "What do you put on oatmeal if not milk?"—I decided to assemble basic nutrition facts along with a bunch of recipes that were so simple that even I was willing to make them. Because of my training schedule, I wanted to spend as little time in the kitchen as possible—minimum meal preparation and with practically no cleaning up after. I found that eating most foods raw was the ultimate in simplicity, and I wasn't the only one who agreed. I published these facts and recipes in my own cookbook, *CHEF*, an acronym that stands for Cheap, Healthy, Easy, and Fat-free (available through my website, www.ruthheidrich.com).

But Where Do You Get Your Protein?

A question I'm frequently asked is "Where do you get your protein if you're not eating any animal products?" The answer is: from fruits and veggies, since all plants have protein. And the amount of protein you get from plants just happens to be the "right amount." If you were to average all fruits and veggies, you'd get approximately eighty percent carbohydrates, ten percent fat, and ten percent protein, which is exactly the proportion of the macronutrients that our bodies function best on, whether athletic or not. You may have heard that athletes need more protein, but you automatically get more when you eat more to offset the increased calories burned with exercise.

Many athletes feel that protein powders are necessary, but that's not the case. If you increase your protein intake through protein powders, you automatically decrease the proportion of carbohydrates. The problem with this is that your muscles' first choice for fuel is glucose and will only use protein when your carbohydrates get too low to meet your energy needs. The body can use a limited amount of protein for energy, but since your muscles prefer carbohydrates (which provide glucose and glycogen), you can keep them from robbing protein needed for repair and maintenance of body tissues. This is known as the "protein-sparing effect of carbohydrates." Don't fall into the high-protein delusional trap!

Not Your Typical Daily Diet

Diet is critical to overall good health, and any athlete will tell you that what you eat is extremely important. You've got to have the proper fuel on board or you'll never feel like running—or much else, for that matter.

Since I adopted a low-fat vegan diet more than thirty years ago, and a mostly raw diet more than ten years ago, I've had lots of chances to modify and fine-tune it over time. I have never found any plant foods that didn't work, but I did find that some offered much more nutrition than others. It was my goal to eat a daily diet that was easy to shop for, easy to prepare, and, most importantly, offered the biggest nutritional "bang" for each calorie "buck." And it turned out that this was the most delicious diet as well.

When I first get up, I make a cup of cocoa-tea, my own version of a delicious and healthy morning beverage. It consists of a mug of hot water to which I add a green tea bag; a rounded teaspoon of hundred-percent pure cocoa powder; and sweeten it with a bit of stevia.

Green tea and pure cocoa are loaded with antioxidants, low in calories, and have just a bit of caffeine. I sip on this while doing my calisthenics and stretches.

Then, after my usual morning mini-triathlon (run, bike, and swim—plus weight-lifting three times a week), I'm ready for my breakfast, which consists of a large bowl of mixed leafy greens—usually including my favorite leafy green, kale—a sliced banana, a sliced-up mango, about a half-inch of fresh ginger cut into small pieces, and a large sprinkle of cinnamon. Over this, I pour the "dregs" of my cocoa-tea, which adds a nice touch of flavoring and is my substitute for a dressing. Because I don't eat breakfast until I've completed my mini-triathlon workout, usually around 10 or 11 A.M., I don't eat lunch.

I don't always snack, since my breakfast is so late. But when I do, the snack consists of raw carrots, an apple, or some other fruit. Because most everything I eat is raw, the water content is very high, and I find I don't need to drink a lot of fluids. (The real test for hydration is not the number of glasses of water one drinks or even the feeling of thirst but, rather, that the urine is clear, colorless, and copious.)

My supper consists of the same large bowl of mixed leafy greens, to which I add a tomato, half of a red bell pepper, a small-to-medium broccoli crown, a handful of mung bean sprouts that I always have growing in my kitchen, some seaweed (usually sushi nori), and more fresh ginger, all topped with a rounded teaspoon of curry powder (my own mix of turmeric, cumin, and chili powder). For a dressing, I use balsamic vinegar and prepared mustard or salsa, sometimes both. Variations from time to time consist of adding dried shiitake mushrooms and raw sweet potato or yam.

My dessert is almost always the same: a cup of blueberries and nine or ten dried plums (prunes to us old-timers) with more ginger and cinnamon. After that, I have a large bowl of air-popped popcorn, no salt or anything else—just plain.

As for supplements, I take none with the exception of vitamin B_{12}, since it is most commonly found in animal products and is actually made by bacteria. I also have never used any of the gels, goos, energy bars, or the so-called "sports drinks." These refined products have all had nutrients modified and/or electrolytes added, whereas "real" food has your needed nutrients naturally. And I believe natural is better!

There's not a lot of variation in my diet, making it simple to maintain, and I never tire of those meals. In fact, I really look forward to each of them, and my theory is that this is what my body wants and needs, and is therefore satisfied. I don't count calories and rely on my appetite to tell me how much to eat. Since there's no cooking involved, there's no cleaning up to speak of. Preparation is fast and easy, usually about ten minutes for each meal, and totally filling.

What follows is a list of each of my foods, which all have lots of fiber, are high in nutrient density, and are commonly available. I highlight just a few of the many nutrients and other benefits they provide:

- **Green tea** has a high content of flavonoids, plant-derived compounds that are a kind of antioxidant. Antioxidants fight against damaging free radicals and are therefore protective of your heart. Green tea is also a good source of catechins, which slow oxidative damage to cells and help protect against cancer.
- **Cocoa** contains flavonoids and phytosterols, which are compounds that reduce cholesterol, and increase endothelial cell function, also helpful for reversing heart disease. The cacao bean from which cocoa is made has an ORAC (Oxygen Radical Absorption Capability) rating of more than 50,000 per 100 grams.
- **Stevia** is widely grown for its leaves, which are used as a sweetener. It's up to 300 times sweeter than sugar, therefore requiring less use, and has negligible effect on blood sugar.
- **Leafy greens** are loaded with fiber, along with vitamins A, C, K, and folate; minerals such as calcium, iron, magnesium, and potassium; and phytosterols that help protect you from heart disease, diabetes, and cancer.
- **Bananas** are high in potassium and manganese and, surpris-

ing to most people, one banana provides about five percent of your daily protein needs.

- **Mangos** are high in antioxidants, vitamins, and minerals. Called "the king of fruit," but unlike many fruits, mangos are rich in vitamin E as well as vitamins A (beta-carotene), B_6, C, and K.
- **Ginger** is a rhizome—an underground stem—and contains phytochemicals that reduce inflammation and nausea.
- **Cinnamon** is high in ORAC values, which means it's a powerful antioxidant. Plus it has carotenoids such as carotenes, zeaxanthin, lutein, and cryptoxanthins. It's also said to normalize blood sugar levels.
- **Tomatoes** contain lycopene, a flavonoid that together with carotenoids, another antioxidant compound, has the ability to protect cells and other structures in the body from harmful oxygen free radicals. Lycopene also helps prevent skin damage from ultra-violet rays and offers protection from skin cancer.
- **Bell peppers**—especially red, orange, and yellow ones—are high in the flavonoids luteolin, quercetin, and hesperidin; and the carotenoids alpha-carotene, beta-carotene, cryptoxanthin, lutein, and zeaxanthin. These last two you might recognize as being touted as supplements for eye health.
- **Seaweed** is rich in potassium, iron, calcium, iodine, and magnesium, which are the minerals concentrated in seawater. It's also one of the few vegetable sources of vitamin B_{12}.
- **Turmeric** contains curcumin, a polyphenolic compound that provides its deep orange color and is thought to have anti-tumor, antioxidant, anti-arthritic, anti-amyloid (think plaques), anti-ischemic (think blood clots), and anti-inflammatory (think of any of the "-itis" afflictions) properties.
- **Cumin** and its abundance of vitamins C, A, and essential oils helps fight infections and has stimulating, anti-microbial, and anti-fungal properties.
- **Chili powder** helps the stomach to create hydrochloric acid

for proper digestion and assimilation of nutrients. It can also relieve constipation by stimulating peristalsis.

- **Mustard** is an excellent source of selenium (which helps prevent cancer), a good source of magnesium (which helps lower blood pressure and restore normal sleep patterns), and a good source of omega-3 fatty acids, manganese, and phosphorus.
- **Salsa**, because it contains tomatoes, is a good source of lycopenes and carotenoids.
- **Blueberries** contain anthocyanins and proanthocyanidins, which are thought to improve memory, learning, and general cognitive function. Some research shows they could slow age-related decline in mental function.
- **Prunes** have been shown to slow resorption of old bone, increase bone density, and help prevent osteoporosis, just from a daily consumption of eight or nine.
- **Popcorn**—plain, air-popped—is loaded with more polyphenols than vegetables and fruit, with the hulls having the highest concentration. It's also high in fiber.

By the way, remember the heart attack that Dr. McDougall mentioned I was at risk of dying from because of my high cholesterol reading of 236? After fewer than three weeks on my new diet, my cholesterol had dropped down to 160 and the next test reading a few months later showed it was 129. It continues to run at that very healthy level, along with healthy readings in all other tests.

Conquering the Negatives and the Blahs

The ability to calibrate and recalibrate your aims is a fundamental skill, no matter what distance you're attempting or at what stage in your running career you find yourself. Consider Ruth's first Ironman. She'd had to rethink her training due to injury. In the middle of the race she gave herself the permission to drop out, once she'd reached a mark that didn't seem too far off. Once she'd arrived at that spot, however, she discovered she had enough energy to set herself another goal. Significantly, at no point in her race—one that tested her body and mind to the limit—did she allow herself to think how many miles she had to go. Nor did she visualize crossing the finish line. Whether consciously or not, she knew that thinking too far ahead would only rewire the brain to consider what was difficult, instead of what was achievable. By concentrating on what she *could* do, she enabled herself to do it—and thereby made the seemingly impossible, possible.

You'll notice that Ruth not only set herself achievable goals, but those goals were based on three-dimensional points: the hotel where her clothes were, the top of the hill. She didn't give herself a time limit (I'll run for just fifteen more minutes) or conjure up an abstraction (I'll run until I feel better). On the face of it, of course, nothing could be more logical than setting yourself reasonable goals. Yet, in the middle of thinking about what you *are* doing, it's surprisingly hard to tune out negative or judgmental thoughts about what you *should* be doing.

One of the most testing parts of any marathon is what is referred to as "hitting the Wall" or "bonking." It's that period of the race, roughly between miles nineteen and twenty-four, when the fitness level you attained during training has been reached, your stores of glycogen have been depleted, and the body starts drawing its energy from the muscles in order to maintain the amount of effort you're expending. Not surprisingly, given that the brain and the body are intimately connected, your entire physical atmosphere changes: your legs and feet feel like lead weights and your mind tells you to stop running. The reason why you've run all those miles in training is to cope with precisely these moments, and to force your body over the Wall until adrenaline kicks in as you approach the finishing line. I've hit the Wall enough times to know that it's not an illusion simply to be willed away.

The Negatives

Ironically, for me, the worst moment of a race may not occur toward the end, when I'm hot and bothered and adrenaline seems to be taking its sweet time to alter my brain chemistry as I anticipate the finish. Instead, it may strike at the very beginning. After I've taken my position near the starting line (or perhaps far away from it, depending on how many runners are taking part in the race) and someone worthy has sung the national anthem, I'm left alone with my thoughts and the race ahead of me.

I invariably discover that the bladder I emptied only a few minutes before has filled itself again. My stomach burbles menacingly, even though I ate the same breakfast that I've eaten before every other race. My body is overwhelmed by aches and pains of a mysterious provenance, in spite of the fact that I woke up that morning with a spring in my step. Worst of all, a host of reasons as to why I absolutely shouldn't run gather in my head. I call them the Negatives, and they're a particularly unpleasant family of armchair blowhards bent on sabotaging my best efforts.

You're in no condition to attempt this race, they say. *You don't belong in this corral. Why did you wear this top? You're sweating already.* Sometimes their observations are contradictory: *You're still half asleep; you should have had more coffee this morning. You've drunk too much coffee, that's why you need to use the port-a-potty.* Invariably, they aim to hit you where you're most vulnerable: *You haven't trained enough;*

why didn't you train more? You're too old and not fit enough to wing it; why haven't you made more of an effort?

Boy! Who needs to hear such things? And they don't even have the good manners to exit stage left as soon as I cross the starting line. *You're running too fast; there's no way you're going to be able to maintain this pace. You're already behind your time; unless you step on it, you'll be nowhere near your goals. Where is the first mile-marker? Was the first mile always this difficult? What are you going to do about that big hill that's coming up? Why does your heart feel as though it's going to burst out of your chest? Why is your breathing so labored; didn't you take your inhaler?*

No matter how many times I run or how much I try to relax and ease into the race, I find it hard to quiet the chatter. Perhaps it's a perverse expression of the drugs—both administered (caffeine) or naturally produced—that are pumping through my body. Maybe I need to see a shrink. Whatever the cause of the Negatives, I'm hardly alone in finding it difficult, as that great sage of human nature Johnny Mercer wrote in different circumstances, to "accentuate the positive and eliminate the negative."

Thankfully, the running itself usually takes over. My body warms up and I find my own rhythm. Some races have been nightmares of forced walks and stitches and mile splits that grew longer and longer. But others have more than exceeded my expectations.

As the adrenaline that propels you forward to the finish line is magically replaced by the endorphins that leave you over the moon with your achievement, you forget all the agony and the doubts that went before, and, as Ruth did with her first Ironman, begin to wonder whether you could possibly run a little bit faster the next time. Like a mother presented with her newborn baby, you forget the pain that accompanied your labor and concentrate on the rewards. The Negatives are silent.

I try not to be a passive victim while the Negatives are tsk-tsk-ing and tapping their feet impatiently. At the start, I take deep breaths to slow my heartbeat (which can help remove stitches) and shake my shoulders, arms, and legs to try to loosen my tension. I consciously attempt to reframe my thinking and con-centrate on the constructive elements of the race. *You've run the distance before, and run it well,* I tell myself. *You've trained hard, and soon enough you'll get into your stride. All will be well. Just run.* I'll also check in with how I'm feeling after one mile or the first lap or the next water station and give myself the option of walking for a while or picking up the pace once I've reached those markers. The true utility of these promises to myself is that they allow me to determine my own race rather than be determined by it, and allow my training to do its work.

These techniques become essential once the Wall looms large. It's at that moment that the Negatives become a full-throated chorus of naysayers, and where you almost have to vocalize your determination to continue and the rewards that await you should you do so:

- *I'll run until that lamppost and then I'll walk.*
- *I'll stop at the next waterstation. . . . OK, the one after that.*
- *Ten steps at a time. One. . . . Two . . . . Three . . . . Four. . . . etc.*
- *I can't believe that eighty-year-old just overtook me. There's no way I'm going to allow him to do that.*
- *She's attractive. Let me see if I can catch her up.*

As you can see, not all of these encouraging words show the runner in the best light. But by mile twenty of a marathon, niceties tend to be cast aside, and you cling on to any strategy that will keep you moving in the direction of the finish line, no matter how politically incorrect or blush-provoking such thoughts may be on recollection.

Sometimes the Negatives can be tricky customers, and lull you into complacency. Such a thing occurred in my first marathon. At mile twenty-two, as one heads south out of Harlem and the northeast corner of Central Park hoves into view, Fifth Avenue—heretofore sedate and flat—begins to incline steadily for a mile. It's a killer slope, not because it's particularly steep, but because it seems to go on forever, right at the period of the race where you feel like stopping immediately. There's nothing to be done but to put your head down, shorten your stride, and grit your teeth until you reach the end of the hill at the entrance to the park at 90th Street.

In 2007, I arrived at that spot and looked at my watch. If I maintained my pace, I calculated, I was on course for a time of slightly over four hours. *That's not bad for a first effort*, said Father Negative. *It doesn't much matter if you're one or two minutes over four hours.* The autumnal oranges, reds, and yellows of the park began to surround me, as I reflected on Pa Negative's thoughtful, supportive observation. My response came through loud and clear. *I haven't run twenty-four miles and up this damn hill to come in at 4:01. I'm going to ensure that my time begins with a "3."* Sure enough, the extra determination spurred me on and I beat the four-hour deadline by seventy-five seconds.

So, grim-faced doggedness has a central role in running. You may not be feeling your most athletic or talented, you may not be particularly proud about how you motivated yourself to get to the end of the race, but forcing yourself to cover the distance can push you into a different space where more positive and pleasant emotions can take over.

Now, we all look for those moments when one's body *is* grace and strength, and running becomes synonymous with the magical, invisible, and literally thoughtless process of *inspiration*. On such fleeting occasions we're at one with the in-and-out movements of the systolic–diastolic, spontaneous synchronization of breath and movement, which allow our bodies to move miraculously through space. If, like me, these occasions don't generally happen until you've finished the actual race, you can try to will it to happen.

I've now run the Miami Marathon twice, and each time I've recorded a personal best. I'm not sure quite why it is—the warm weather in January, the flat course, the running along South Beach as the sun comes up—but I tootle around this baby with a smile on my face. Even a dreaded out-and-back diversion onto a causeway at mile twenty-three hasn't been able to dampen my mood. It's partly because I don't feel pressure to perform. It's also partly because I sometimes force myself to grin, actively observe and enjoy the scenery, and even find myself amused by the artful wickedness of course designers. These constructed moments not only make the race more satisfying but they've surely improved my time.

If I'm honest, most of the time I struggle to maintain my equanimity. The Brooklyn Half-Marathon, which is run in May, circles Prospect Park twice before heading down the broad boulevard of Ocean Parkway to Coney Island. It's a great course and a wonderful way to celebrate where I live. Prospect Park is as leafy and hilly as Ocean Parkway is flat, and in 2011, as I made my way around the park under a hazy sun and in ninety-six percent humidity, my pollen-induced asthma kicked in. I found myself forcing each in-breath and propelling each out-breath, my heart thumping against my ribcage and the Negatives shouting that I'd never be able to maintain this pace and that I should stop and walk home. I had a medical condition, they reminded me. Didn't I know that it had rained the night before and my asthma was always bad the morning after a storm?

This happened last year, I told my stern admonishers. *And I was fine once I got out of the park. It'll be the same. Just trust me.* The Negatives gave a shrug and merely folded their arms that much more tightly against their chests. I eventually made it out of the park, and ran a personal best for the race and the half-marathon. As it turned out, for all my labored breathing, I'd never run faster in the park itself.

The Blahs

If you run for any length of time and over a long enough distance, there'll come a point in a race or training run when you'll experience what is technically called *misery*. Your breathing isn't smooth and regular; your limbs ache; your digestive system is acting up; and your mind and heart just aren't in it. We all have those days, and sometimes the best thing to do is simply to chalk the run up to experience and hope that tomorrow's effort will be better. That said, it's worth pointing out a few options that might make those days fewer in number and less intense when they happen.

First, the running blahs could be because your training is out of whack, or you're bored of the courses you regularly run, or you're running alone. As Ruth has suggested, try scaling back or altering your training by swimming, lifting weights, cycling, practicing yoga, or generally mixing it up. Run another route, or find a friend or join a group to go out with you.

Secondly, you might be overdoing it and you need a rest. Sleep and relaxation are vital components of running well and keeping fit. You may not be eating properly, or enough. Consult a nutritionist or your doctor. If you're really out of sorts, then stop running for a while, until your mojo comes back. Or, conversely, run a race to pump yourself up and get you raring to go again.

Thirdly, watch videos or subscribe to magazines that feature runners. You can find training tips, inspirational stories, and other reasons why you should get out there again. It's worked for me.   *—M.R.*

Running Ruins Your Knees— and Other Body Parts

Run when you can,
Walk when you have to,
Crawl if you must,
Just never give up!

—**Dean Karnazes**, author
of *Ultramarathon Man*

Knees **are basically unstable and vulnerable because** they're hinge joints, bending only one way, and that is backwards. Knees don't bend sideways or front-ways or even twist. This is unlike the greater mobility of our shoulder, wrist, hip, and ankle joints. There's no question that as we age, knees frequently give out. However, it's not due to running. In fact, runners typically have healthier knees than non-runners. While you run, the alternate loading and unloading on the cartilage causes *perfusion*, an increase in the circulation into the knee joints through a "pumping" action.

A study supporting this contention is cited in note thirty-two: James Fries, M.D., coauthor of a 2008 study from Stanford University that tracked 528 runners and 423 non-runners, found no greater incidence of knee replacements or knee problems in runners. So why are knees often the first joints to go? Aside from the obvious variety of knee injuries that can occur, there's the effect of our diet on our knees. Foreign proteins from animal foods can get trapped in the joint's synovial fluids and cause the inflammation that's known as arthritis. In some cases, we develop what is called "leaky gut syndrome." What normally would be prevented from being absorbed into the bloodstream from our gastrointestinal tract slips into our circulatory system, and sometimes from there into our joints. Our ever-alert immune system is supposed to identify and destroy these foreign proteins, just as it would identify and destroy bacteria and viruses. The process by which it does this is inflammation, by sending white blood cells to attack and destroy those foreign proteins. With that come swelling, heat, redness and, worst of all, pain—all well known to those who've been diagnosed with osteoarthritis of the knees.

Although all this grief is assumed to be due to wear-and-tear or even just "aging," I'm betting that unless you're following a vegan diet, it's little bits of cow, pig, chicken, fish, and cow's milk proteins getting stuck in your joints. I can attest to this because five years prior to my cancer diagnosis, I'd been diagnosed by a rheumatologist with "osteoarthritis." I'd been prescribed a powerful non-steroidal anti-inflammatory drug for it. When I stopped eating animal foods, the arthritis disappeared. I haven't had even the slightest hint of arthritis ever since. I would love to say that research has since shown that a low-fat vegan diet is an effective treatment, but, sadly, I could find none. (Something to consider is who might sponsor such research when there's no money to be made from it.)

Running Injuries

Most running injuries fall into two classes, accidents and overuse. As for the first—well, accidents happen. Most runners I know have had their share of bad days and suddenly found themselves flat on the ground, wondering what happened. It may have been that lip on the sidewalk or a root sticking up on that trail. During the hectic start of races, runners can trip up other runners by mistake. I've had every one of these experiences. The good news is that fit people recover much more quickly from injuries that result from accidents.

The second type of injury, overuse, comes from doing too much too soon, going too far, or too fast. Knowing your limits is tricky because I've found that our bodies lie to us all the time. Mine will tell me that I can go on forever, and the very next minute I'm ready to quit. Other times, I'll have some kind of ache or pain and feel that I shouldn't run, but when I go out for a jog anyway, that ache or pain is gone in minutes. My body might tell me that I'm healed and could go back to the level where I left off, but my mind knows otherwise.

Keeping a journal is important so that you can accurately monitor your distance, workouts, pace, and state of health for all your body parts, not just the ones that hurt. The main point is that, sooner or later, most runners will suffer some kind of injury. The best treatment I've found is rest—as difficult as that is at times. If you don't give your body time to recover, understand that it'll *take* the time!

The most serious injury I've ever sustained was not while running, but while biking. I was cycling down a road in Hawaii, training for my next triathlon, when a truck carrying a load of kitchen cabinets came toward me and made a sudden left turn as the driver realized that he'd almost missed the street for his delivery. Since I was coming from the opposite direction and happened to be smack in the middle of the intersection, the truck plowed right into me. The next thing I knew, I was flying through the air, and when I landed, I was in excruciating pain.

I looked down at my left leg and saw a bunch of bumps that turned out to be parts of my tibia, the lower leg bone, which had been shattered where the truck's bumper had hit me. The mere raising of my head caused extreme pain in my right hip. My first thought was, *How am I ever going to recover in time to do that triathlon in three months?* My next thought was, *This could ruin my goal of running sixty-three races at age sixty-three, beating last year's record of sixty-two races at age sixty-two* (!). Someone yelled frantically, "Call 911!" Within just a couple of minutes I heard the wail of sirens and an ambulance appeared. I was soon on my way to the hospital.

My injuries were devastating. X-rays and an MRI showed that my left leg had a comminuted fracture, meaning that it had broken into many small fragments. The ER doc said that if you were to drop a china cup on a concrete floor, that's what it looked like. I had three cracks in my right pelvis where I'd landed after being thrown into the air. As badly off as I thought I was, the doctors marveled at the fact that I was still alive. They told me that if I'd not been so fit, I probably would have been killed. The worst part of it was that because the fractures were on both the right *and* left sides of my body, it would be impossible to even stand or walk, let alone run, for six to eight weeks. The orthopedist said that if I agreed to let him put a titanium rod in my leg, I could at least be on crutches and do some weight-bearing on the left leg as the pelvis healed. The decision was a difficult one because of the major trauma necessarily done to the leg in implanting the rod through my knee. After consulting several other doctors, I agreed to the surgery.

As I worked through months of a long, very painful recovery, my orthopedist was grave. "You need to face facts," he said. "You'll be lucky to walk again. But you'll never get back to running, much less back to racing." The second orthopedist I saw had as his pronouncement "Find another sport." These words immediately called to mind that horrible day of my breast-cancer diagnosis, sixteen years previously, when I was told that I might not have much longer to live because the tumor was so large and aggressive.

My response back then was to change to a vegan diet and start training to do the Ironman Triathlon. My response to this new pronouncement was to double my visits to my physical therapist. My medical insurance covered physical therapy twice a week, so I added two more sessions a week and paid for it myself. I also knew that I had to get in the pool where I could do water-supported running while my fractures healed and to maintain my swimming. I also continued my cycling on a stationary bike, trying to keep my fitness levels as high as possible. The healing, incidentally, occurred in half the estimated time the doctors had given me. I credit this to the bountiful leafy greens I ate, which provided minerals to the bones, and the increased circulation from the additional physical therapy, water-running, and my own version of triathlon training.

Despite having to miss the triathlon I'd been training for when the accident occurred, the investment in intense rehabilitation still paid off handsomely. I knew there was no way I was going to be off my crutches in time to enter any of the track events in that year's upcoming Senior Olympics, so the next best thing for me to do was to volunteer to be a timer. But as I watched each of the different events, I got an idea. Why not run the 100-meter dash—on my crutches? The race director said I was crazy, but I talked him into letting me do it. I'm sure that it was quite a sight as the announcement was made for the runners to take their mark at the starting line, and here I came, making my way on my crutches.

When I finally took my place and the gun went off, I hobbled off as fast as I could. I tried not to get too far behind, but I also realized that if I weren't very careful, I could fall and re-fracture those not-quite-healed bones. Of course I had a dismally slow time, but I made it. And, since I was the only one in the 60–64 age-group, I won another gold medal!

My recovery accelerated as I continued to get as much exercise as I could in the form of my own mini-triathlon. In addition to the daily water-running, I increased the number of laps in the pool and my exercise-bike resistance and time, gradually working up to several hours a day. I looked forward to being able to race a "real" race again.

Active Recovery

It seems to a lot of us runners that injuries because of overuse happen at the most inopportune times. Back in the 1980s, I was a reporter for *Triathlon Today*, a national news magazine for the developing sport of the triathlon. I wrote articles on the different triathlons that took place on Oahu, including the many that I participated in. Once, I was scheduled to run a race but got a hamstring pull that was so serious that my doctor said I shouldn't run for at least four to six weeks. I informed my editor that, sadly, I wouldn't be able to cover this triathlon because of my injury. His response surprised me. "Why don't you cover it from the back of the pack?"

I thought this was a great idea. Here was an opportunity for me to still be able to participate and do my job as a reporter. I knew that the swim was no problem, nor was the bike portion of the race. It was only the running segment that would cause me grief, but I was able to walk without pain, so that was what I decided to do.

It had been a little over two weeks since I'd run. I continued my daily swimming, biking, and water-running. In the same way as when I'd broken my leg and pelvis, my hamstring healed in almost exactly half the time that had been estimated by my doctor, a benefit I attributed to my fitness level and diet.

So, there I was at the starting line. The gun went off, and I completed the swimming and biking portions with little difficulty. Then when the transition to the running portion came, I felt so good that I thought I'd just start running and stop at the first hint of any pain in my hamstring. I certainly wasn't worried about my time or place in the race. I purposely went slower than race pace, chatting with the other "back of the packers," those who knew they'd never place and were doing the triathlon just for the fun of it. I, too, was having fun from this new vantage point. As the finish line came into view, I realized that my hamstring had not uttered a single complaint, that I'd actually run the entire distance.

The real surprise was, not only did I have an article for my editor after all, but I also received a gold medal since, again, I was the only one in my age-group!

As you can tell, I really believe in the concept of "active recovery." Yes, an injured body part needs rest, but it also needs a supply of healing nutrients delivered by increased blood circulation. And how do you increase circulation? By exercising the parts of the body above and below the injury to the greatest extent possible. For example, with my hamstring injury, my daily exercise regimen pushed the blood supply through the injured tissue without stressing it and, as a result, it healed faster than if a total rest had been enforced.

Another example of active recovery is based on research that shows that injured tendons and ligaments react in their healing differently depending on whether or not they are subjected to stress during the actual healing process.[23] If there is a tear in a tendon or ligament and it's subjected to *some* stress, the repair cells line up with the stresses that are normally applied to that tendon or ligament, so that it heals in a correct fashion. Otherwise, with no stress applied to the healing tendon or ligament, the repair cells line up in a random fashion, resulting in a weaker repair.

This principle of active recovery applies to soft-tissue injuries, which are most of the injuries that runners suffer from by doing too much, too soon. Fractures are, of course, another matter, because putting stress on a healing bone can set back the healing process. I've had a number of fractures as a result of being hit by trucks twice. In each case, I immediately got into the water and exercised the parts of the body that were unaffected. For example, with an injured leg and pelvis I swam using just my arms. With an injured arm that resulted from falling after tripping on a crack in the sidewalk, I swam by using the unaffected arm and used the lower body to kick.

Swimming this way also contributes to "muscle memory." The nervous system still sends stimuli to the injured side and keeps that part of the system working, so that when the bone heals, you can get back to normal that much more quickly. In my active recovery I also was aware of the pain levels of the fractures, noting that as the weeks went by and as the pain lessened, I could very gradually start using the arm or the leg as the bone healed. This helped it regain its strength much more rapidly.

Being injured and unable to train was frustrating, even knowing that one day the injury would be healed. Each morning I'd wake up and wonder if this was the day. For example, in the case of the fractured hip, I was told it would take six to eight weeks to heal but I felt sure that I would heal faster than that, based on previous experience.

So after a couple of weeks, I'd test the hip each morning for signs of pain. I kept trying every day, knowing that one of those days soon there would be no pain, and I wanted to know exactly when that day was. Sure enough, the hip was healed in three weeks, and if I had not tested it until the six weeks had passed, I would have missed three weeks of training. The lesson? I got back to my training regimen the first day possible, much sooner than predicted, and saved my sanity!

Now, here is another CYA statement: *None of this should be construed as medical advice on how to treat injuries.* With my healing fractures or hamstring injuries, I was told by many that I was "crazy" to take such risks, that I should just "rest." I, however, felt that I knew my own body better than anybody else and was pretty sure I understood its limits. I was prepared to deal with whatever results I got. Fortunately, things turned out well for me. You, however, are the one who knows your own body the best, and you should have a physician check it out.

Daily Running

You've probably heard that you can't run every day; that if you don't have a recovery day in between runs, you'll get injured. Back in 1968, when I was running on my own without any guidance or coaching, I enjoyed my daily runs and never felt the need to take a day off to recover. Even after races, I would run the next morning. My runs may have been a bit shorter and slower, but I always thought that a day without running was like a day without sunshine. I also found that my high-carb vegan diet allowed me to recover much faster as well.

The real logic behind this thinking is that you need about forty-eight hours to repair muscle damage. The trick is, however, most people don't stress themselves nearly enough to do any muscle damage. You'll know it if you do, as you'll have DOMS (Delayed Onset Muscle Soreness) with its symptoms of soreness and stiffness. If you do find you have a case of DOMS, then you should take a day or two off to recover—in fact, you had better if you want to avoid injury.

The Aging Runner

Aging is not an injury per se, but it's certainly easier to injure yourself as you age. A problem that can arise as we grow older is the loss of the fat pad at the ball of the foot. Notice how a baby's foot is chubby with lots of fat around it. As we age, we start to lose that fat. I first encountered this around the age of sixty, when I noticed a pain in the ball of my foot. My orthopedist then enlightened me as to what was going on, prescribed an orthotic, and told me to back off on my running for a while and maybe consider another sport. I certainly wasn't about to give up what was my favorite sport. I found that padding helped quite a bit, so soon enough I was off and running again.

Along with Terry Shintani, M.D., and Dr. Diane Nomura I've been a co-host of a local weekly radio talk show on nutrition and fitness for over twenty years and been privileged to interview some very knowledgeable guests. One who particularly inspired me was gerontologist Patricia Blanchette, M.D., who told me that everything we formerly thought was due to aging has turned out to be either *disease* or *disuse*. This struck a particular chord with me as I've found it to be quite true. *Disease* is most often caused by the wrong diet and *disuse* is lack of exercise, clearly exemplifying one of the basic laws of physiology, good old Wolff's Law again, *Use it or lose it.* So whether, for example, you suffer from heart disease, diabetes, arthritis, or osteoporosis, the symptoms of those conditions are almost always diet-related and, therefore, reversible. Knowing this should provide the motivation to eat the right diet and get effective exercise on a lifelong basis.

Then there's the old stereotype of what we mean by telling someone to "Act your age." I got a real dose of that when I did a race less than a week after my breast reconstruction surgery. Because I was healing so well, I decided it would be okay to run a 10K race that next Sunday. All went well and I figured that no harm was done—until the following morning. When I woke up, the surgical site was a bit swollen, so I thought, just to be safe, I'd have the surgeon check it. When he found out what I'd done, even before looking at his handiwork, he actually yelled at me, "When are you going to start acting your age?" and stormed out of the exam room. I was stunned and then I got mad! *For Pete's sake, I am acting my age*, I told myself, *and I'm not some old, stuffy, matronly, sedentary . . . This I think is what my age is* supposed *to look like: fit, active, energetic, taking on challenges. . . .* The nurse then apologized for his behavior, chuckled, and said, "He'll get over it." Thank goodness, when he calmed down and came back to check me out, he said, "You're darned lucky you didn't do any damage, but, please, at least give it another week or two to heal." So, I think these many years later, I'm still "acting my age."

Older runners, however, typically find that they're slowing down. This is certainly true of myself. I was embarrassed the other day when a twenty-something-year-old passed me, *walking*! Research suggests that it's primarily stride length that shortens. In general, though, I'm happy that I can still run and often remind myself that there are lots of seventy-somethings who *can't*.

I don't want to give the impression that I am always up for my daily mini-triathlon, that my motivation never flags, and that I never have to talk myself into doing my daily run. There really are days when I don't feel like it and that's when I tell myself to at least get out there for a walk. Usually, all it takes is to see a green light that will turn amber and then red if I don't start running to make it, and once I start running, I usually don't stop. That's a little secret that I discovered about myself and think that it might apply to you as well. Works every time!

If you really want to be inspired, take to heart the story of Indian-born Briton Fauja Singh. Fauja liked to run in high school, but political turmoil and a hard life of manual labor in India prevented him from doing any more until grief at losing a son propelled him onto the track and the road when he was in his mid-eighties. He discovered that running provided him with solace, purpose, and companionship. He started running marathons at the age of eighty-nine, and was nominated to carry the Olympic torch for the 2004 Athens Olympics. In October 2011, Fauja stunned the running world when he became the oldest marathoner to complete a marathon. He ran the Toronto Waterfront Marathon at the age of one hundred in just over eight hours, after setting world records in distances from 100 meters to 5000 meters only seventy-two hours earlier. In April 2012, at the age of 101, he completed the London Marathon in 7 hours and 49 minutes. A Guinness World Record holder, Fauja Singh follows a plant-based vegetarian diet and credits it with his success.

Or, you can take some encouragement from Mike Fremont, who at the age of ninety-one completed the Knoxville Half-marathon in a time of 3:04, a single-age world record. He was clear as to why and how he was still breaking barriers in his tenth decade, as *Runner's World* reported:

Fremont, who looks like a spry 60-year-old, attributes his longevity to a vegan diet. "Training is important," he told *Running Times'* Mike Tymn, "but when you get to be my age, you're not going to be able to train at all unless your body holds up. I simply cannot overemphasize the importance of the plant-based diet to my performance."[24]

These are wonderful examples of truly "lifelong running."

Run Your Run

As you've probably noticed by now, Ruth and I are competitive. We like to do well, and we like to do better than well. That said, if there's one thing that both of us want to illustrate over and over again in these pages, it's that success and failure are relative, and to crow obnoxiously over your achievements or beat yourself up over not accomplishing something is not only counterproductive but, to quote Mr. Spock from *StarTrek*, illogical. No matter what time you record, everyone in that race started at the same place and ended at the same finish line. You may not have come in first, but you probably didn't come in last. And, even if you did, you beat every single person who dropped out. And, even if you didn't finish, you still did better than everyone who didn't show up at all.

So, even though I don't like to underperform in a race, I tend not to hold on to my dissatisfaction too long. After all, no one forced me on to the course, and another run always awaits. Instead, I keep in mind lessons provided by Ruth, Fauja Singh, and Mike Fremont. Sometimes you have to wait a very, very long time to be the best!

The great, leveling aspect to running is that, in any given race, it's a very good bet that someone is faster than you and someone is slower—at least according to the age-graded calculator. Yes, you may be surrounded by runners and fearsome competitors, but in the end you compete only against yourself—your younger self, your older self; your fatter, thinner, or exactly-the-same self. No one else is going to run your race for you. As the Nike slogan says, "Run your run."

—M.R.

You Can Only Run Under the Right Conditions

"It's the road signs, 'Beware of lions.'"

—**Bernard "Kip" Lagat**, Kenyan distance runner, on why his country produces so many great runners

*T*he kind of running we've talked about in this book is always planned. But isn't it nice to know that you could escape lions if you had to? There'll almost certainly be times when you'd planned a run, but for some reason you don't really feel like doing it. Most of us are pretty good at rationalizing and coming up with all kinds of reasons *not* to do something. It's too cold. It's too hot. It's too windy. It's raining. It's snowing.

You've probably heard the myth that you can't run in cold weather because you'll freeze your lungs. I was told that back in February 1973, when I was transferred from Hawaii to Wright-Patterson Air Force Base in Ohio. Once people found out that I was a daily runner, they told me not to run in these wintertime temperatures: it was too dangerous; I'd freeze my lungs. I'd never been exposed to sub-zero temperatures before, and lacking the knowledge and experience, I went directly to the base's flight surgeon to find out if it was really true. He laughed and said our nasal passages warm the air before it gets to our lungs, and that the only people who had to worry about running in those temperatures were men—and wearing a fur codpiece would take care of *that* problem!

I found running in snow to be some of the most magical experiences I'd had. When it was deep enough and there were no tracks, I could feel and hear the crunching under my feet. If it was early morning, the streetlights cast eerie, almost surreal shadows. Dawn was the best time to be out in the snow, alone, appreciating how beautiful a fresh coating can be.

Even so, whenever the temperatures dipped really low, I'd arrive at the office to be greeted by "I bet you didn't run *this* morning!" There was one occasion, during the record-breaking "Great Blizzard of 1978," when temperatures fell to twenty-nine degrees below zero *before* the wind chill was factored in. There was also a record-breaking snowfall of twenty-eight inches. To be honest, if I'd known that such records would be broken, I might have re-considered going out *that* morning. The truth was, however, I'd get up at 5 A.M. *every* morning, don my winter-running apparel, and head out the door for my usual hour-long run. I recall that it seemed to take longer for me to warm up that morning and I did a lot more slogging through deep, wet snow than usual!

When I heard the weather report later on the way to work, I thought of the saying, *No such thing as bad weather, just not enough clothes.* And speaking of clothing, at those extreme temperatures I wore a sweatsuit over long underwear, a T-shirt, a running jacket, a parka, two pairs of gloves, two pairs of socks, and a balaclava. With these in my wardrobe, I never missed a day of running due to extreme cold weather. And yes, again my office mates said, "Well, I bet you didn't run *this* morning!"

Hydration

At the opposite end of the temperature scale is heat. Higher temperatures lead to greater loss of water in the form of perspiration, which can lead to dehydration. It's especially important to replace the lost fluids with water, since a loss of too many is life-threatening. A good test of adequate replacement of fluids is to weigh yourself before you run and then again afterward. The amount of weight you lose is the amount of water that needs to be replaced. You'll also discover if you were drinking enough while on the run.

An equally effective way to see if you're dehydrated is to check your urine. My rule of thumb, as I said earlier, is C^3—that is, your urine should be clear, colorless, and copious. The darker yellow the pee, the more you need to drink. Water is the ideal beverage, and you really don't need to worry about replacing electrolytes (sodium and potassium) unless you sweat a lot or are going on a very long, hot run.

Fresh, raw fruits help solve dehydration because they're about eighty-five percent water. They also provide electrolytes and the carbohydrates to fuel your run. For long runs, take some bananas, orange slices, or dried fruit, and a water bottle with you. If you're really serious about your long runs and have no water source, you might invest in a camelback, a backpack with a built-in straw that you fill up with whatever you want to drink. That way you don't have to stop to rehydrate. Just be careful when swallowing, because it's easy to choke.

Believe it or not, you can drink too much water! My good friend Claudia was so conscientious about drinking water that she ended up in the hospital with hyponatremia—a serious condition. Hyponatremia occurs when the electrolytes in your bloodstream become too diluted from drinking too much water. Weighing yourself before and after your run gives you important information in this case as well. In the event you weighed more than when you started, it might be because you were drinking too much water. With a little practice, you learn how to judge the right amount.

Never Give Up

One excuse for not running that I've used a few times is when it's raining. On occasion, I've gotten out of bed, put my running gear on, gone to the front door and seen that it's pouring. Rain is, for me, much more of a challenge than snow, cold, or heat. I tell myself that I'm going to get wet with sweat anyway, why should it matter? On rainy days I really have to give myself a talking-to. I recall that old saying, *The pain of discipline is nothing compared to the pain of regret.* And out I go!

Once, I almost didn't follow my own advice. On another of my frequent Sunday morning races, I awoke to the sound of rain coming down in buckets. I wanted nothing more than to crawl back under the covers and forget the race. That thought lasted all of two minutes as I recalled how eagerly I'd anticipated the Manoa Valley 5K, a race I'd run each year for quite a while. When I arrived at the starting line, the rain had eased up just a bit, but it was clear that a lot of people just hadn't shown up. The starter's gun went off, and we were running.

The first turn was about a half mile up the road, and as my friend Howard and I made the turn, he yelled, "Don't look now, Ruthie, but you're the first-place female!" Keep in mind that I was in my sixties at this time and had long given up ideas of being one of the elite (top three overall) winners. But when Howard said that, my heart really started pounding. *If I ran really, really fast,* I thought to myself, *I might be able to maintain that position.*

The rest of the race was agonizing as I kept waiting for what I was afraid was the inevitable—a younger, faster female passing me. However, I never saw another woman. As I crossed the finish line, I excitedly ran up to Sam, our finish-line scorekeeper, and asked him if I really was the first-place female. When he told me that indeed I was, I reminded myself that I'd won this gold medal only because I ventured out in heavy rains when most others didn't.

I wasn't the only one who was shocked by my first-place finish. This same friend, Claudia, was traveling and stopped at the Denver Airport. While waiting for her flight, she picked up a copy of *USA Today* and later told me that she couldn't believe her eyes. There was a news item about Ruth Heidrich, a sixty-six-year-old woman in Hawaii, placing first female overall in a race. The lesson? Never give up!

Another example of never giving up, no matter how hopeless the situation seems, occurred one morning when I arrived at a race too late. Most races in Hawaii start at 7 A.M, especially the smaller, shorter ones. The Hard Rock 10K was a new race in town, and I signed up for it as soon as the entry forms were available, a couple of months beforehand. I normally arrive at the starting line about half an hour before the race begins, which is just long enough to check out the scene and do a little warm-up.

This time, however, was different. As I rolled up to the start area for my usual routine, there wasn't a single runner in sight and the race officials were taking down the cones and tables. I was shocked and couldn't believe my eyes. "What happened to the race?" I cried. They pointed down the street where I could see the tail end of the mass of runners about a half-mile up the road.

Heartbroken, my first thought was *Darn, I've missed the race.* My second thought was, *Wait a minute—maybe I haven't! If I run fast enough, I might be able to catch up with at least the tail end of the group.* So I took off, reminding myself from now on always to check race details, especially the start time (6:30 A.M. in this case)!

As it turned out, I managed to catch up to the rear and gradually made my way up toward the front of the pack. The good news was that because, as usual, there were very few older female runners, I still achieved first place in my age-group, another gold medal, and another lesson in never giving up.

On Running and Writing

When I'm not running, I spend a lot of my time reading other people's writing, or doing my own. I've come to see many parallels between these two pursuits—even though at first glance it would appear that two more different pastimes couldn't exist. After all, one involves constant movement while the other requires sitting down for long periods of time. You certainly don't have to be physically fit to bash away on a keyboard, and you certainly don't need to be literate to fly o'er hill and dale. In fact, who among us hasn't indulged in the stereotype of the dumb jock who needs a Cyrano de Bergerac to wax poetical or, conversely, peddled the Romantic cliché of a writer as a sickly and pallid purveyor of aperçus, whose most strenuous exercise is plucking a flower or lifting a strong cup of coffee to his lips?

Actually, caffeine can be a useful stimulant in running (many of the gels you pick up at sports stores contain it), so perhaps the writers are on to something! But, more seriously, running and writing have more in common than you might think. First, they both require discipline and practice: they demand that you show up rather than procrastinate or talk, talk, talk. Secondly, they take time. Just as no one expects you to ease into a marathon the first day you put on your sneakers and head out the door, so no one imagines you'll be able to compose a book in twenty-four hours, or a week, or a month, or even two. You run a couple of miles, you put down a couple of thousand words; then, the next day, you cover a little more distance. Before you know it, you've started to move faster or with more assurance, on both the road and page, and what seemed impossible to contemplate begins to emerge before your eyes.

Because both activities necessitate a slow accretion of skill and stamina, they lend themselves to anxieties (such as the Negatives I mentioned earlier) and to a competitive spirit that may be healthy or not, depending on whether you use it to hone your craft or bewail your own inadequacies. It's also likely that unless you discover an extraordinary talent in either area, you'll probably not find yourself on a podium or receiving a literary prize. These realities make it even more important for you to discover the satisfaction to be had through crossing the finish line or expressing your ideas accurately and compellingly.

Both running and writing should lead to a humble acknowledgment of the geniuses who made what you do look effort-less, and to a recognition of the hours of agonizing hard work that most likely went into enabling them to achieve what they did. One of the masters of both has to be the Japanese nov-elist and essayist Haruki Murakami, who has not only written books of dazzling complexity, imaginative breadth, and great length, but has completed a number of marathons, an ultra-marathon or two, and several triathlons. (My inexactness here is mainly due to the fact that by the time you've read the last sentence, he'll have taken part in quite a few more!)

Murakami has a refreshingly undramatic attitude toward the task of writing or running—he simply starts and carries on going. It's not that he doesn't experience difficulties en route and doesn't find himself deeply challenged, but the novelist, who claims that most of what he knows about writ-ing he learned through running every day, seems to *trust the process*—relishing the simple pleasures of putting one foot or word after the other and realizing that nothing will be accomplished unless you commit to keep going during the rough times. And I agree. You'll have a chance to edit your piece later on, just as you'll have an opportunity to analyze just what went wrong at mile three once the race is over. In the middle of your course and your book, don't let your inner censor stop you from moving forward.

So, running and writing are far from mutually exclusive, which is why it's best to put aside one's preconceptions of what a writer or a runner looks like: a hollow-cheeked obses-sive circling the track for endless hours or a hunched, bleary-eyed loner staring at a blank computer screen.

Finally, although good form is important in running and writing, and you can find trainers in both activities to pro-vide you with useful tips and keep you focused, you always start both journeys where you are rather than where you should be, and make the best of what you've got. You don't need to give up your bodily integrity for your corpus; and your magnum opus needn't be composed at the expense of your health. Make either your own, or embrace them both. Whether you compose or run with music or not, whether you run 5Ks or marathons or write blogs or the Great American Novel, all that matters is that you do what works for you and you have fun doing it.   *—M.R.*

Running Isn't a Real Sport

"A marathoner is a marathoner regardless of time. Virtually everyone who tries the marathon has put in training over months, and it is that exercise and that commitment, physical and mental, that gives meaning to the medal, not just the day's effort, be it fast or slow. It's all in conquering the challenge."
— **Mary R. Wittenberg**, president of
New York Road Runners (NYRR)

How **many times have you heard people say that running** isn't a real sport? Sure, it doesn't involve balls, bats, or other such equipment. It doesn't require a special uniform or super high-tech clothing—except maybe your shoes. You can do it by yourself or with other people. There isn't even a point system. But running *is* a competitive sport: Just ask anyone who's ever run a race. And it's the only competition that I know of that allows participants to contend with relative equals. Women only compete against other women; men just against men. Even children get to participate, and all only within their own age-group. There's even big money to be won for the elite winners. Had it not been canceled, the 2012 New York City Marathon would have offered the largest amount of prize money in history: $853,000. Even if you can't run, you can still compete—there are even wheelchair and handcycle divisions.

I experienced firsthand the possibility of competing without running a few years ago. I was somersaulting on a trampoline when I landed with full force on a pointed toe and fractured the navicular bone in my foot. The accident occurred on a Saturday night, with a race the next day for which I was the race director, so I had to show up. My plan had been to fire the starting gun, drop it, and begin running. However, by the time I got the X-ray diagnosis from the emergency room, it was far too late to call someone to tell them that they'd have to take over for me. The next morning I showed up on crutches. Since we had a lone male wheelchair entrant, we therefore had a wheelchair division. Kim was extremely competitive. He even had a high-tech wheelchair that he used for races—in addition to his regular one, from which he transferred himself.

As everyone was lining up at the start line, I got an idea. Here was the empty, regular wheelchair that was seemingly begging me to climb into it and race. I asked Kim if I could use it. His reaction was one of total surprise, and then puzzlement, before he told me to go for it. I fired the start gun, dropped my crutches, and took off in his wheelchair. It took a while to get the knack of keeping it straight, but I eventually managed to work up a head of steam. Even as I was still heading out, I could see runners at the turnaround coming back. As they saw me tootling along, their faces initially registered shock and surprise; then they gave me the thumbs up. Because we had police escorts, I was privileged to have a police car driving slowly behind me, making sure I was safe. Of course, I was in last place overall, but at least I was participating.

As I made my way to the finish line, a great cheer erupted from the crowd. I teared up as I realized that even when I couldn't run, I could still compete. What was even more amazing was that since I was the only entrant in the Female Wheelchair Division, I got—guess what?—a first place and another gold medal!

Getting to the Starting Line

Once you've started to really enjoy running and want to test your limits, you might sign up for a local road race. A 5K (3.1 mile) race is short enough to be fun while being competitive enough to test your mettle. Your local running store is sure to have information about races—some local and short; others all the way up to international marathons. Allow a good lead time to train for them, at least three to four months, but remember to fill out the application form and pay the entry fee. Most races now allow you to apply online, so there's no excuse for delaying. The main thing is to make a commitment that keeps up your motivation to train.

The next step is to plan a training schedule. There are all kinds of schedules, from three days a week to all seven, from track workouts to long runs on the road, to sprints or interval training, to laps around a track, and you can find many of them online. Depending on your weekly mileage, a theoretical schedule *could* look like this. Keep in mind, however, that trial and error will help you decide what will work best for you:

DAY	GOAL
Monday	Run three miles
Tuesday	One-mile speed workout on a track
Wednesday	Run two miles
Thursday	Run three miles
Friday	Run one mile
Saturday	Run five miles
Sunday	Run, bike, or swim—or rest

My earlier recommendation of getting up, getting dressed, and getting out the door obviously precludes eating. This has always worked for me for several reasons. First, I'm never hungry until late morning, after my workout. Second, I consider sleep time critical for health and sanity and would even rather sleep than eat—at least early in the morning. And, third, I love the feeling of being lean and mean, light and fast, a sensation I have when I don't eat before a run or a race. If that doesn't work for you, then fruit is, in my opinion, the best food to eat beforehand. Try it both ways and see what works best for you.

Competition—Racing Against Others or Just Yourself

There's nothing like the challenge of seeing how you compare to your peers. I've also found that running with a group motivates me to run faster and longer than when I'm just out on my own. Another source of motivation is seeing one's rate of improvement. This is where a watch comes in handy. If you know how fast you ran a given distance last time, it's fun to see if you can beat that time today. If you enjoy doing that, you're on your way to becoming a fun but serious runner.

Age-groups are one of the best innovations in races. This is when you race against others in your age-group and gender. (You'll have seen a representation of this in Martin's commentary in chapter four.) Age-groups usually run in five-year age increments, going in some cases up to the 100–104 age-group (a very elite segment, indeed!). The good news is, the older you are, the smaller the group, and the better your chances of winning a gold medal. The secret is to outlive your competition! As you'll have seen throughout this book, this is one of the main reasons I've won more than a thousand medals in my many years of competition—including sixty-seven marathons, six Ironman Triathlons (four Kona Ironman, one New Zealand Ironman, and one Japan Ironman), and dozens of other types of races that include track meets, 5Ks, 10Ks, 15Ks, 25K, 30Ks, ultramarathons, a pentathlon, sprint triathlons, Olympic-distance triathlons, duathlons, biathlons, and lots of bicycle and swim races. For me, getting to the starting line of any race really stirs my competitive juices and motivates me to give it my all.

The Olympics

For many people, the ultimate sporting event is the Olympics. I was fortunate enough to attend the Seoul Olympics in 1988 as a guest host for the American contingent. I got to eat and sleep in the Olympic Village, where I welcomed and gave orientation sessions to athletes and attendees. When the games got going, I attended various venues to watch the actual competition. Being a runner really paid off because much of my daily running was going to and from these different locations. It was in the Olympic Village where I got a real taste of not only how serious these competitors were, but also how dedicated their families and support crew were. The Olympics, it turns out, is inspiring for everyone.

It wasn't too long ago that there was no such event as the Women's Marathon. It first became an official event in the 1984 Summer Olympics in Los Angeles. I remember well the challenges that the winner, Joan Benoit Samuelson, faced qualifying for the Olympics and then contending with a knee injury and surgery. That was when I first heard of the therapeutic effect of water-running.

Another Olympian who inspires me is Abebe Bikila, who won the marathon in Rome in 1960. I find his story so stirring because, as he stood at the starting line, barefoot, other runners mocked him and even the TV commentators speculated on how fast he'd be able to run without wearing shoes. His bare feet sped over the hot streets of Rome in a then world-record time of 2:15:16 and earned him a gold medal. People realized that success is not about the shoes but the training, technique, and diet.

As a high-school swimmer and diver, I had aspirations of competing in the Olympics. I had to drop those dreams due to the demands of real life, and I thought they were gone forever. However, after I finished a race one day back in 1997, my friend Ken Wheeler told me that I ought to compete in the Senior Olympics, which I'd never heard of but which got me excited. After doing some research, I found out that the next event was to be conducted in about six weeks in Las Vegas, Nevada, and would be one of the state qualifiers for the nationals. I sent in my application and booked my flight and hotel. I entered both running and triathlon events and won four gold medals, which qualified me for entry into the nationals, which were to be held in Tucson, Arizona.

Activities in the Senior Olympics parallel the "real" Olympics, even to the Parade of Athletes, where participants from each state get together, carry their state's flag, and march in as a group. While states such as California and Texas had hundreds of participants, I had trouble finding my state, Hawaii. Since the states were arranged alphabetically, I figured I shouldn't have any difficulty locating my home. However, it simply wasn't there. I went to the organizer and asked where the Hawaii contingent was. "You're it!" she said. She handed me a large banner marked HAWAII in large letters, and told me to get in line in front of Indiana, which had brought another large delegation. It felt so strange. Here were all these hordes of athletes—and then there was me! I swallowed hard, took a deep breath, and carrying the Hawaii banner high above my head I marched into the stadium filled with thousands of people.

All of a sudden I heard a tumultuous roar: yelling, whistling, and cheering. I realized that the crowd was giving me, the lone athlete from Hawaii, a tidal wave of a standing ovation! Television cameramen walked backwards in front of me and reporters asked me what it felt like as I made the entire 400-meter circuit. I was so choked up I could hardly speak. I was brought to tears as I realized my Olympic dreams had come true. I knew that this was a moment I would never forget!

The Marathon

by Martin Rowe

As part of the preparation to run my first marathon, I attended a seminar hosted by New York Road Runners (NYRR) for those of us who, as 26.2-mile virgins, were anxious about our first date with the race and wanted to make sure we weren't going to show up with bad breath or spinach in our teeth. We were welcomed ("Hands up those doing the marathon for the first time. Yay!" *Scattering of applause*). Then, one of the lean and peppy experts on stage told us that, as far as she was concerned, three sorts of runners took part in a marathon.

The first and smallest group, she said, consisted of those athletes who were *racing*. They were, in the insistently assonantal world of competitive sports, "in it to win it." We mortals may have caught glimpses of these gods of tarmac and concrete when we'd watched the race on TV or as spectators in a previous year. But, suggested our coach, we'd almost certainly not meet them on the course, since their times would be in the 2:03- to 2:13-hour range for men and 2:15- to 2:25-hour range for women. In effect, the elites would be sprinting every mile in five minutes . . . and faster. (*Gasps all round.*) Among these superstars were the wheelchair and handcycle competitors, some of whom would zip around the five boroughs of New York City in eighty or ninety minutes. (*Eyes opened a little wider.*)

The second group, continued our cheerful leader, was made up of the large number of individuals *running* to beat their own personal bests or build points for their running clubs. They'd probably taken part in at least one marathon, had competed in races before, or had been rocking the road for quite a few years. This group encompassed everyone from sub-elites to those trailing in an hour or ninety minutes behind them.

The third group, concluded the instructor, was us—the folks interested in *completing* the marathon. We might run the entire length of the course. We might walk part or even all of the twenty-six miles. We might do it on our own or with a posse. We might totter around on stilts or crutches. We might wear the coolest gear or a fright wig or both. We might dress in combat fatigues or in a banana-skin costume. We might run for charity, personal redemption, or to cross an item off our bucket list. However we chose to finish this race, the specialist stressed, we should understand that, whatever our physical abilities or challenges, whether we were aiming to be world champions or to break four hours or simply wanted to get a medal, all of us had just as much right to be on that course as anyone else. All of us had different goals and training tasks. All of us would be gaining a different experience from the race. And all of us were marathoners.

What our cheerleader didn't tell us was that marathoning (if I may employ such a word) hadn't always been so inclusive. Although Boston had been holding the race since 1897 and Chicago since 1905, by the early 1970s marathon runners in the United States were still few on the ground. They accurately considered themselves (and were thought of by others) as cranks and die-hards who covered unimaginably long distances for the love of competition and the challenge of the course. Certainly, they couldn't have been doing it for the money or fame, since there was precious little of either.

The 1970s changed the image of running in the United States. In 1972, Frank Shorter won the gold medal in the marathon at the

Munich Olympics, and was pipped at the post by the East German Waldemar Cierpinski in Montreal in 1976. In 1977, Jim Fixx published *The Complete Book of Running*, and turned jogging into a national health craze. Jimmy Carter took up the sport, although a photo of him looking drawn and under duress during a 10K race in 1979 may have been one of the nails in the already ferrous coffin of his presidency.

Marathons had been staged in New York City for a century. In fact, the first one in the United States finished at Columbus Circle in 1896. There were indoor marathons and endurance races, but it took Fred Lebow, whom we met earlier in this book, to see that running needn't be only for the elites and oddballs. It could appeal to recreational runners like himself who were never going to be sub-2:30 athletes and yet who enjoyed the challenges, freedom, and reduction in stress that long-distance running could deliver.[25]

Lebow joined New York Road Runners, and took part in the Cherry Tree Marathon in the Bronx in 1970, where NYRR was then based. The conditions were less than ideal. In training and during races, NYRR members competed with automobiles for the road and kids would occasionally amuse themselves by throwing stones at the unfortunate contenders. Lebow suggested that the marathon be moved to Central Park in Manhattan, where there'd be less car traffic and more chance of the runners being seen and supported. Later that year a marathon was staged there.

Lebow had found his mission, and began to promote the race far and wide. The numbers taking part grew exponentially. By 1975, the race was too big for Central Park (it was hard to race with ease when you were dodging baby-strollers and horse-drawn carriages, pedestrians and bikers). A colleague at NYRR suggested to Lebow that as part of the United States' bicentennial celebrations the race could be run through all five boroughs, beginning in Staten Island and then proceeding through Brooklyn, Queens, Manhattan, and the Bronx, before ending at Tavern in the Green in Central Park. It was a huge logistical and financial challenge that NYRR and Lebow—who knew just whom to call, ask for sponsorship, and bring on board—managed to pull off.

Lebow's triumphant mix of populism and elitism mapped perfectly his attitude toward running, and the marathon in particular. Lebow combined passionate dedication to the ideal that you didn't need to be sporty to benefit from running with the belief that New York City's race could attract the greatest talent in the world. In so doing, he made it possible for the ordinary to follow quite literally in the footsteps of the extraordinary.

Lebow didn't confine his vision for the marathon to the region, or even the North American continent. He visited running associations throughout the world and encouraged their members to take part in the marathon, scouting talent among international athletes and persuading them to compete in New York City. What had been a parochial experience for a few local runners in the Bronx became in a few years representative of a city that took in the world's refugees and turned them into New Yorkers—at least for a day. That the race ran through communities as diverse as the city itself was part of the genius of Lebow's vision: a fractious world came to a fractious city, so that both might see the possibilities of cooperation and coexistence—in the streets the runners streamed through, and in the company in which the individual athletes ran. The marathon was as gritty as the streets it covered, in a burg that by the mid-1970s had been wracked by rising crime, indebtedness, and political dysfunction. The rise of the marathon seemed to reflect—and perhaps even stimulate—the rebirth of the city.

Lebow understood the possibilities of "event marketing" *avant la lettre*, and built the marathon into a multi-million-dollar sponsorship opportunity. Even in those instances where he got into fights, a certain knowing playfulness existed amid the acrimony. In the 1980s, Lebow involved himself in a kind of meta-competition with Bob Bright, coordinator of the Chicago Marathon, over who could stage the biggest and best race. Each tried to poach the other's elite runners, expand their numbers, and offer the greatest experience for everyone taking part. For all the braggadocio, both men secretly knew that the "fight" between them only made their events in particular and the sport as a whole that much more visible.

The world of elite marathon running is now dramatically different from four decades ago. Top athletes can now compete to win the World Marathon Challenge, which entails attaining the best positions in the Boston, Berlin, Chicago, London, and New York marathons over a calendar year. Prize money runs into the hundreds of thousands of dollars, and live TV and Internet coverage, as well as sponsorship from sportswear and other firms, ensure that top athletes can earn considerable amounts of moolah. But the world has also changed for the Fred Lebow–level runners. In forty years, and especially in the last decade, interest in running marathons has exploded, and turned the race into not only a sport in which *racers* can win medals and break records but one where runners and completers alike can get something to hang around their neck and conquer their own personal goals. It's also become a way to raise millions of dollars for many charities.

And marathon running isn't just about big-city races. A whole world of local marathons exists, where you don't have to win the lottery, raise lots of dough for charity, or qualify with a special time to get in. According to marathonguide.com, January 2013 offered you the opportunity to choose from thirty-six marathons all over North America—in addition to the international marathons, half-marathons, and shorter distances being staged at the same time.

This massive expansion bears witness, of course, to the exponential increase in the numbers of people taking part in them. In New York City's first marathon in 1970, for instance, 127 runners attempted to run four-and-a-bit times around the outer loop of Central Park. Only fifty-five finished, a dropout rate of forty-three percent. In 2010, by contrast, 45,350 people moseyed over the Verrazano-Narrows Bridge and made their way through the Big Apple. A mere 247 didn't cross the finish line, a completion rate of 99.45 percent. (One of those 247 was Ethiopian superstar Haile Gebrselassie, holder of twenty-seven world records, who pulled out with a knee injury at mile seventeen. So, one should be careful about judging the ability of that .55 percent!)

Such a change in what it means to "run a marathon" hasn't been without controversy. For years before the sport's sudden popularity, the race—whose mythic origin was the messenger Pheidippedes' cross-country scramble from Marathon to Athens to announce the Greek victory over the Persians in 490 BCE—was something that only a select few could, or would, do. Almost by definition, the marathon carried with it the notion that unless your heels were blistered, your muscles wrecked, and your mind half-crazed through exhaustion and dehydration, then you hadn't really done the thing. (Indeed, that Pheidippedes was reputed to have expired after delivering his news only added to the grim glamour.)

Given the paucity of publicity or prize money for marathon runners back in the day, perhaps the *only* satisfaction available lay in the knowledge that you'd sweated, toiled, and wept your way for a distance more than four times the length of the longest track event—and that you were among the very few for whom such an outcome was desirable. Then, distance running often meant you wore your old (unsponsored) running shoes and a raggedy shirt, which failed to wick the sweat away from your skin. There were no gels or sports drinks, few if any water stations, no mile clocks, no musical bands, no "cheering zones," few supporters, and the most rudimentary of first-aid stations. You might even have had to weave your way through traffic, with no police escort or clear demarcation between you and the public pathway. And all this was after months of intensive training, which may have entailed you getting up in the dark at 5 A.M. and slogging your way through bitter cold, searing heat, or sapping humidity. (As I watched *Run for Your Life*'s footage of runners trailing through wintry Bronx streets in the mid-1960s it was hard not to shudder at how miserable, cold, and lonely the event seemed.) At such times, cheering crowds or medals or international glory must have seemed very far away.

It was probably inconceivable to the competitive runners of the early 1970s that huge businesses would sponsor marathon running or that hundreds of thousands of dollars of prize money would be awarded—let alone that elite runners would be able to gain revenue from sponsorship and endorsements. Or that the humble New York

City Marathon would turn into the biggest race in the world, involving, according to *The New York Times* in 2010, twelve ferries, 500 buses, "1,694 portable toilets, 42,000 PowerBars, 90,000 bottles of water and 563 pounds of Dunkin' Donuts coffee beans, enough to make 45,000 cups." And that was before we runners even got on the course! During the 2010 event itself, "62,370 gallons of water, and 32,040 gallons of Gatorade [were] served in 2.3 million paper cups." We were entertained by 137 bands, timed by 106 clocks, and 52,000 medals and food bags as well as 60,000 heat sheets awaited us once we finished. In 1970, about a hundred souls watched Gary Muhrcke cross the finish line in first place in a time of 2:31:38. In 2011, the number of people estimated to watch on the course (let alone on television throughout the world) was over 2.5 *million*.[26]

The somewhat dirty little secret as to why so many cities and regions now offer marathons is not that they've fallen in love with running and want to encourage citizens to become healthier and more active—although these might be added benefits. These races attract individuals with disposable income to a location, where they spend money on hotels, restaurants, museums, and shopping. The result is a cash infusion and tourism bonanza that provide municipalities with a great deal of bang for the bucks that they invest, given that the event itself usually lasts less than a day and there are few fixed costs (such as a stadium to build or maintain). If sponsors can be prevailed on to cover the physical needs of the runners, then all a city has to worry about is traffic control, policing, sanitation, and emergency services. In 2009, the Chicago Marathon generated $150 million in economic activity.

Not surprisingly perhaps, some have complained that marathons have lost their connection to the city they represent. Over fifty-seven percent (26,000) of those who entered the 2010 New York City Marathon were from overseas, the majority of them brought to the city on tourist–running association packages, which included hotel accommodation and guaranteed entry into the marathon. Of course, making the marathon a global event was part of Lebow's mission, but perhaps even more persuasive a reason to bring the world to the city than reflecting Gotham's already international flavor is that runners, their families, and friends (especially the out-of-towners) contributed an astonishing $340 million to its economy in 2010. Given that New York City's marathon caps the current number of runners at around 45,000, it's becoming increasingly difficult to get in (in 2010 over one hundred thousand people from around the world applied through the lottery) if you're not on the tourism package, running for the specially designated charities, or able to fulfill the guaranteed entry requirement of nine NYRR races plus one race at which you volunteered.

Lebow's vision has succeeded beyond even his wildest dreams. Hundreds of thousands of ordinary men and women huff and puff around hundreds of marathons and half-marathons throughout the country, and claim their medals and heat sheets. In reaction to this, some are now looking to ultramarathons, trail races, or assault-course-style events to recapture what they took to be the free-wheeling, nonconformist identity that once attached itself to the marathon. Has running become merely another way to sell consumers lots of swag? Is it now simply another manifestation of a trend where what was once a test of excellence and discipline beyond the ordinary has become a celebration of mediocrity and a culture of self-esteem gone mad?

Those questions became very real in November 2012, when a week before the scheduled marathon Superstorm Sandy tore through New York City, bringing devastation and death to several neighborhoods, including parts of Staten Island, from which the race was due to start. The City and NYRR prevaricated over whether the race should be run before calling it off two days before the start date—by which time many runners were already ensconced in their hotels and criticism had been leveled at the very organization that had made marathon running so popular throughout the world.

Although there were good reasons to hold the race (it would raise morale, it would bring hundreds of millions of dollars to the city, it wouldn't divert resources from the clean-up and rescue), neither the optics nor the atmospherics were good. Bodies were still being retrieved from the shore near Fort Wadsworth, where we runners would assemble. The fact that tens of thousands of us would spend a considerable amount of energy leaving Staten Island as quickly as possible across the Verrazano-Narrows Bridge symbolized the isolation Staten Islanders felt from other parts of New York City. The gesture would reinforce one of Ruth's memes that marathon runners were self-obsessed and entitled narcissists. Many of us who were slated to take part felt terrible. We didn't want to run, and a substantial number of people posted on forums that they didn't want us to run, either. The race was meant to celebrate the city, and nobody felt like celebrating.

The cancellation of the 2012 New York City Marathon brought out the best and worst in runners. Some didn't seem to recognize that holding a race amid such devastation might be considered insensitive. Others organized themselves into groups of volunteers and went to the areas affected to help with the clean up. Groups of us ran for local charities involved in helping out after the storm; we tidied up parks and doled out supplies in affected neighborhoods. The decision to halt such an iconic race seemed to crystallize the debate over just what running now meant: was it a pastime for the rich and self-indulgent? Had big-city marathons lost their soul in their attempts to push more and more people round a course for more and more money? Had we all lost our perspective?

These cavils echo other schisms within the running community. Some grumble that the slower completers of marathons negate the achievements of those who've put in the time and effort to run faster.[27] Certainly, one can't say that the 45,350 who finished the 2010 New York City Marathon were all fitter or faster than the fifty-five who completed the course in 1970, since the former were running on average more slowly than the latter. While records have continued to be broken at the business end of the race, a study reported on in *Running USA* found that the average speed of marathoners overall had decreased from three and a half hours for men and four hours for women in 1980 to 4:16 and 4:43 respectively in 2009.[28]

One reason people cite for running the marathon is that it connects the ordinary individual with the world-class athlete, since you're running on the same course. In the big-city marathons, where the route is often lined with cheering onlookers, running a marathon can make you feel like a superstar—at least for a few hours. But are you really running the same race? Some think not. They argue that the valorization of the ordinary schmo encourages showboating rather than a serious dedication to perform to the best of one's ability on the day. After all, Pheidippedes' (possibly apocryphal) achievement depended not merely on the fact that he died immediately after delivering the news of the Athenian victory or that his announcement was so brief, "We have won." The sheer number of miles he covered (175, if you include the distance he ran from Athens to Sparta and back to seek assistance against the Persians), the significance of what was being said, and the time it took for him to complete the journey gave the message its weight, and perhaps was the reason why the story survived.

But who's to say that unjustified and unworked-for fame is not as attractive an ambition as a superhuman feat? Consider, if you will, the Cuban-American Rosie Ruiz, who in the 1979 New York City Marathon apparently decided that it was far too much effort to run the whole course and took the subway instead, hopping on to the course so she could cross the line in just under three hours. The next year, Ruiz enterprisingly joined the Boston Marathon about a mile from the finish and came in first (in 2:31). Commentators were amazed at how fresh the relatively untoned Ruiz appeared and at how little she knew about the training regimen she claimed she'd followed. They were astonished at how she'd managed to knock more than twenty minutes off her time the previous year. When you're an elite runner, you measure your personal bests in increments of seconds. Ruiz was, literally, too good to be true.

Ruiz has always maintained that she ran her races fair and square, so it's difficult to pinpoint exactly what her motivation was. Ironically, if she was looking for the fame her "accomplishment" would bestow on her, she succeeded beyond her wildest expectations. Even thirty years later, her name is synonymous with deception and double-dealing, one reinforced by her later arrests for embezzlement and involvement with cocaine.

Lebow, who was known to cut corners himself (even if not as literally as Ruiz), was devastated that somebody would ruin the integrity of his race. It seemed never to have occurred to him that anyone would want to cheat. Yet Ruiz was in some ways the shadow incarnation of Lebow's conviction that you didn't need to be a runner to triumph in the marathon. Ruiz merely decided that you didn't need to sweat it to be famous. She wanted to be incredible, and she was—because no one believed her despite her protestations of innocence. It's ironic that Ruiz became the face of a race despite having not been seen by anyone during it (!), and that in spite of her never running a major event after Boston, she's the ordinary runner whom everyone remembers.

Ruiz's deception ushered in a host of measures—electronic tags, cameras, and other items—that communicate data and video to ensure that no one will be able to do what Ruiz did. Even so, every year—perhaps in every race—a number of folks run without paying the entry fee or using someone else's bib. Or they burst from the crowd to garner the cheers from the crowd or get the feeling of what it means to cross the finish line, without bothering with the quotidian nonsense of actually training or taking part as a fully paid-up participant in the race. These last, *very late* entrants are usually tackled before they get very far. But these sleights of hand show that marathoning is not immune to trickery and false impressions.

Yet another complaint about the contemporary U.S. marathon scene is that it has compromised the excellence of American runners. From 1970 to 1982, every male winner of the New York City Marathon was

an American. Since then, an American man has won it only once—
Meb Keflezighi in 2009—and even then there was unpleasant and
racially tinged muttering about whether the Ethiopian-born runner,
who came to the U.S. when he was twelve years old, was a genuine
American, whatever that might mean. American women triumphed in
every New York City Marathon from 1971 to 1977, and haven't done
so since. No American man or woman has crossed the finish line first
at Boston since 1983 and 1985 respectively.

American men and women have been more successful in Chicago,
having won more times than any other nationality (although only five
times since 1990). Even so, that achievement pales in comparison
with Kenya's athletes, who've broken the tape eleven times since 2000.
Since the inaugural year of 1981, only one American woman and two
American men have won the London Marathon, and even though the
Berlin Marathon has been staged since 1974, an American has never
won it. (Americans have been more successful in the wheelchair and
handcycle divisions of these races.)

How, some ask, has there been such a fall-off since the 1970s and
early 1980s, when Nina Kuscsik, Miki Gorman, Joan Benoit Samuelson, Bill Rodgers, and Alberto Salazar were on the winners' podium in
New York and Boston? Some point out the obvious fact that the races
are more competitive now because they feature a broader cross-section
of international world-class athletes. Others comment that American
elite runners are, on average, running more slowly than those of two
decades previously, and so blaming the foreigners doesn't cut it. Some
suggest that there hasn't been enough marketing of personalities, and
that Americans need to see a rivalry between two greats—such as
was the case with Bill Rodgers and Frank Shorter in the 1970s—to
become inspired and deepen the field. Others put the dearth of genuine competitors down to the fact that American runners have poor
"form" (or technique) and that inadequate coaching at middle-school,
high-school, and college levels contributes to the failure of U.S. runners to reign supreme.

Still others argue that the mass-marketing of marathon running in the United States has turned a race that used to be about speed and endurance and genuine sacrifice into one of silly costumes, event management, and the feel-good stories of hosts of ordinary people running to achieve a mediocre time with the bare minimum of sacrifice or pain. Young athletes searching for a genuine contest, they add, now go elsewhere to become part of an elite.

This last proposition is intriguing, if somewhat sour, and seems wrong to me in any number of ways. It's a hard to see how any genuine athlete wouldn't be inspired or challenged by the extraordinary success of East Africans in long-distance running to want to beat them. I can understand how, if you were an old-timer from the early 1970s, you might look on contemporary marathoners with a certain bemusement. It's a whole lot easier for runners now, especially in the big-city marathons. The roads are closed off, the supplies are plentiful, the first aid is ubiquitous, and you're not (as you were in the first New York City Marathon run outside Central Park) required to climb up and down steps. The staggered starting system and the use of corrals for runners of different paces mean that most people taking part in the large marathons aren't overly impeded. The only downsides are that some areas of the race now have so many runners coming through that the roads aren't wide enough to accommodate them and the spectators who crowd in on either side. Anyone who's been one of the thousands who shuffle with stiff legs and sore bodies for up to thirty minutes to collect their clothing bags after crossing the finishing line at Tavern on the Green in New York City will recognize that handling the volumes of mid-packers is still a work in progress.

So, I don't begrudge those who reflect on how tough they had it way back when and envy the runners of today. Nonetheless, those who claim that we who have had mediocrity thrust upon us don't know the meaning of marathons are misguided. Sure, some budding athletes may look at the organizational hoopla that surrounds the race and think that it no longer has the cachet of, say, the hundred meters dash or stardom on the basketball or tennis court. But plenty of young Americans of both sexes are competing at the highest level, and the significant prize money available to the top athletes should provide the talented with some incentive. Perhaps this dearth of winners is merely a cycle waiting to turn.

What we have here, of course, is a question of interpretation—of what the marathon is, whom it is for, and what one's purpose is in running it—all of which are contestable issues. After all, even the distance (twenty-six miles, three hundred and eighty-five yards) has a certain arbitrariness about it. When the modern Olympics began in 1896, the run staged at the inaugural games in Athens covered the twenty-five miles between the town of Marathon and the Greek capital. When the games came to London in 1908, Britain's Queen Alexandra let it be known that she wanted to be able to watch the runners from Windsor Castle (which added an extra mile to the course). Not to be outdone, her daughter-in-law Princess Mary thought it might be rather fun if the competitors ran an extra lap once they reached the stadium (thus the 385 yards). So, while we plebeians have to thank the aristocracy in the form of Baron Pierre de Coubertin for reintroducing the marathon to the world in 1896, we also have them to blame for adding a wholly unnecessary 2,145 yards to the experience. I fancy that the wives of kings Edward VII and George V might have been less enthusiastic about contributing to the pain had they been running the race themselves.

As for me, sitting in a puddle of anxious perspiration at that seminar, the instructor's observation that we were all marathoners came as a huge relief—as I'm sure it did to the other neophytes. We didn't want to bring the marathon into disrepute. We didn't think we were a threat to the gods who gathered at the front. They'd be competing in a race that was their own. Nor would we pose problems for those who wished to break the three-and-a-half-hour mark. They weren't attempting to beat us; they were on the course to conquer the clock; and the corrals and different departure times would mean that we wouldn't get in their way.

We also took umbrage at being dissed as schlubs and barely-also-rans. Given the amount of time we'd be on the course—exposed to the elements, moving our tired muscles, and hitting that asphalt and concrete—we actually stood to undergo a much more grueling encounter with the marathon than our speedier confrères, precisely because our bodies were less well-trained than those of the quicker runners. In fact, we thought we were doing the "true" athletes a favor. We were part of a very long tail, one that made the front end of the race appear even more elite, and the parabolic bulge in the middle nearer to the top than bottom.

The three-and-a-half hour marathoner who sniffily thought we were ruining her race by breaking our imaginary tape at five hours would back in the early 1970s probably have been bringing up the rear, and subject to the same criticisms she was now leveling at us ho-hum harriers. Now, because of our efforts (or lack thereof) she was hovering near the top fifteenth percentile. In short, we might wheeze and rasp and have body parts that wobbled as we stumbled around the course. But we'd make everyone faster look good, and we'd *still* be marathoners.

Furthermore, as I stood alongside the British soldier dressed in combat fatigues and bearing a forty-pound fully-loaded kit bag on his back waiting for the 2009 New York City Marathon to begin, it seemed beyond churlish to think that the soldier (who was raising money for a charity supporting his wounded comrades) wasn't running the race "properly" because he dressed inappropriately and might not break the four-hour mark. Why wouldn't he inspire someone to be the best they could be?

In his bestseller *Born to Run* and elsewhere, Christopher McDougall heaps scorn on the road races of the big-city marathons for their genericism[29]: how they bamboozle us into paying large amounts of money to enter; how we're bombarded with sweat-shop-made shoes and compression socks and water belts, colored iPod holders and over-priced running shorts, cute T-shirts and other tat; and how, once we've begun the race, we're herded from start to finish through lifeless city canyons and off-ramps and underpasses to be given a cheap piece of metal and an energy bar as we cross the finish line and then yelled at to keep moving.

For McDougall and the rebel athletes he champions, downing pizza and a brewski of the cold stuff before escaping the constraints of shoe sponsors (or shoes for that matter), medals, and conventional distances for forbidding mountains and treacherous slopes in appalling weather is what life is about. What's so magical about 26.2 miles of pitch anyway, even if it comes with the royal seal of approval and a gong? Why not 150 miles of joyous free-range running through gorges and over summits with only the limits of your body and imagination to keep you company?

I can sympathize with such sentiments, just as I can recognize how the old-timers must feel looking at the masses swarming up and down the avenues. After all, as Ruth makes clear, isn't running a natural means of expression for children? Why do we have to be *taught* it? Are we all, therefore, simply fools who've been gulled by the corporate running worlds into spending money on trying to become accomplished at something we've no hope in getting genuinely skilled at, and yet which is at the same time our birthright to reclaim?

Well, as both a dyed-in-the-wool democrat and cultural snob who knows there's nothing new under the sun and is willing to try it, I think it's OK to sharpen the point and broaden the base of the pyramid of skills and talents in both endeavors. I think it's perfectly respectable to set your own running goals, modest though they may be. It seems to me, the aim should be to absorb whatever information or insight is available to help you accomplish your task without losing your way. Techniques can be learned, regimens can be established, and targets set. Who knows what benefits they may deliver?

I think it's a valid wish to perform in such a way that you don't embarrass yourself. True, you may not be the wildman or madwoman of long-distance running. You may not suddenly emerge from the masses to overtake the world's best. But even modest accomplishments should be noted. One should experience some reward for doing the basics well, even if you're the only one giving yourself a pat on the back. One's yards should be counted and, if a medal is available, then why shouldn't it be placed around your neck? And if you call yourself a *marathoner*, why should it be of concern to anyone else?

As it turned out, the instructors that day in 2007 had a larger purpose in mind than making us feel good about ourselves. They wanted us to match our expectations with our preparedness levels. If we desired to run the race in under three hours, then we'd need to do a certain amount of training and be at a certain level of fitness. If we aspired to complete the marathon in under four, then we'd have to train for a different number of hours and weeks; under five, and it would be different again. As the evidence of the 99.5 percent completion rate suggested, any of us could *complete* the marathon, even if it meant walking the entire course. What we needed to determine, she told us, is whether we were interested in *running* it as well.

I've talked at length about the politics of the marathon (elite specialization versus democratic populism), not only because I think they're interesting and add a little spice to the quotidian process of putting one foot in front of the other, but because it's virtually impossible to enter any kind of race as a thinking person and not become aware that running is not a wholly neutral activity—even though anyone can do it.

As it turned out, two weeks after the canceled 2012 New York City Marathon, I took part in the second annual Brooklyn Marathon, which circumnavigated Prospect Park in nine loops. The race was as logistically vernacular and as casual as the NYC Marathon is complex, sophisticated, and intense. Instead of a cannon sending off 17,000 of us in the first wave accompanied by the recording of Ol' Blue Eyes singing *New York, New York*, Steve Lastoe of New York City Runs stood on a ladder with a megaphone and an air horn and ushered the 500 or so entrants along Center Drive. Instead of millions cheering us on, a couple of hundred spectators dotted around the Park did the honors. Little yard signs at the side of the road helped us figure out which lap we were on. These *aide-mémoires* were supplemented by eight rubber bands, which began the race on my left wrist and migrated one at a time to my right one each time

I passed a particular water table. Although no bands of the musical sort accompanied my anti-clockwise circuits and no serried ranks of spectators roared me across the finish line, I had a blast. It reminded me that, whether you want the big-city-marathon experience or like your races unadorned and intimate, you'll have the chance to run, record your time, and still get a medal at the end. And you can thank Fred Lebow for that.

Running Is Boring

"When the world is too much to take—I run to rest
from it. When the world doesn't have enough to give me—
I run to work harder for it. When I'm bored—I run for something to do. When I'm overworked—I run to escape too
much to do. When I'm sick—I run to feel better.
When I feel great—I run to feel greater."

—Kerra Quinn, runner

As we've seen, research shows that running is beneficial to the brain. The increased circulation stimulates the thought process, and probably lowers your risk of stroke and dementia. Just knowing these powerful benefits keeps running from being boring for me. In reality, running has opened my eyes to the world around me, both literally and figuratively.

At the time I started running in 1968, I was a graduate student, a part-time guidance counselor at Hickam Air Force Base, and the mother of two teenagers. This meant that I was constantly mentally challenged: trying to maintain a 4.0 GPA, helping students decide what to do with their lives, and handling two adolescents. Need I say more? My early morning runs gave me time for me to be myself and take in my surroundings. Living in Hawaii gives me an appreciation for the natural world—the gorgeous tropical flowers, the swaying coconut trees, the constant greenery, the clear blue skies, and the cobalt blue ocean. I jokingly call the process of looking at the landscape I run through as "surveying my kingdom."

During the first run after my surgery for breast cancer, I surveyed "my kingdom" with new eyes. I was overcome with the sense of how lucky I was to be alive, to be able to see the beauty that surrounded me. The ocean and the sky had never seemed so blue, nor the lush foliage around me so green. It was a transformational moment and gave me renewed joy. More than forty years later, I feel the same way. For me, running can never be boring as long as I'm still able to appreciate life.

Running Really Pays!

I've joked for years that running pays. Really! Then I'll pull out a penny or a dime that I've found along the running route. Every once in a while it'll even be a bill. One early New Year's Day run, I found a $20 bill just lying on the side of the road. It's amazing how often I, and other runners I know, find not just money but all sorts of things cast off along the way. Just yesterday I was putting together some papers for a presentation and could not find a paper clip anywhere. Guess what I found on the sidewalk on this morning's run?

I often joke about my "running errands" as well. People frequently talk about running errands, but they rarely mean it literally. I run to the post office. I run to the bank. I run to the farmers markets. I run to the grocery store. I run to deliver book orders as long as my destination is reasonably close and takes under a couple of hours to reach. In other words, running errands saves a lot of gas money as well as wear and tear on my car—another way that running really pays, literally as well as figuratively.

Running, along with a healthy diet, can also pay off in the drug store. The other day I walked down the aisle and was amazed at the variety of potions, pills, and nostrums on display. I saw items that purported to treat dandruff, acne, headaches, halitosis, sinus problems, acid reflux, indigestion, constipation, diarrhea, hemorrhoids, arthritis, joint pain, sagging libidos, and body odor. I also saw megadoses of vitamins, fiber supplements, fish oil, adult diapers, and so on. And all this expense doesn't hold a candle to the exorbitant costs of prescription drugs! It amazes me to think of all the money I'm saving by not having to buy any of these things. It's sad that most people are spending a ton of money trying to buy good health off the shelf and will probably never figure out that it's their lifestyle that's causing most every one of these problems.

Running pays in another tangible and monetary way, and that is in saving on clothing bills. Most races have finisher T-shirts, which are usually either in a pre-race packet along with all the instructions, or they are to be collected at the finish line. The shirts are usually very colorful and emblazoned with that particular race. Most of us are very proud wearers of T-shirts that promote that hard-earned effort. I just returned from a tabling event where I wore one of my Ironman Triathlon–finisher shirts and found that a lot of people stopped to ask questions about it. I think the T-shirts make the events come more alive when people can read "Honolulu Marathon Finisher" or "Mountain Trail 50K Finisher" or even "Race for Life 5K Finisher." They're often conversation-starters, as people want to know more about either you or the event. I've got more than a thousand T-shirts and cherish every single one of them!

Running Round the World

One of my biggest enjoyments is running in locations that most people just dream about. There are places where running is the best way to appreciate where you are and to realize the benefits of being fit enough to go where so many others can't. I've run around the base of Mt. Rushmore in order to see the giant sculptures of four U.S. presidents from all sides. I've run around Old Faithful at Yellowstone National Park, seeing that spectacular gusher from every angle possible. I've run up and down the insides of the volcanoes Haleakala and Kilauea in Hawaii, run partway up Mt. Everest in Nepal, chased the

Bay of Fundy's fifty-three-foot tides in Canada, and run along fjords in Norway. Being healthy, fit, and having an adventurous spirit is the best way to view this wonderful planet we live on. Boring? Hardly!

Having been a logistics manager in the U.S. Air Force and having traveled a lot for my job, I've developed a love of seeing new and especially exotic places. Unfortunately, the requirements of the job precluded my doing much sightseeing in Alaska, Japan, the Philippines, Korea, Okinawa, Wake Island, Hawaii, and most of the Air Force bases all over the U.S. The one saving grace in seeing these new places was my usual morning run, wherever I happened to be. Once I retired, I decided I was coming back to these places and going to as many others as possible.

Here are more of the unique adventures I've had in my running career:

- Running up and down the 5,000-foot runway at Kunsan Air Base in South Korea, joined by a smiling, uniformed, complete-with-combat-boots Korean soldier
- Running on the Great Wall of China in 1983, shortly after my breast-cancer diagnosis, and having the time of my life
- Running the original Olympics marathon course in Athens, Greece, in the footsteps of Pheidippedes, the first marathoner
- Running up the intricately carved Buddhist temples in Borobudur, Indonesia, to a magnificent view of the rain forest from the top
- Running around Stonehenge, that enigmatic, prehistoric structure of monoliths, before being stopped halfway by guards
- Running along the coast of the Arabian Sea near Muscat, Oman, in the middle of an extremely rare thunderstorm
- Running up the longest and highest sand dune in Namibia
- Running on board a ship as it passed through the locks of the Panama Canal, then swimming in the ship's pool so that I could say that I swam in the Panama Canal!
- Running in Casablanca and stumbling upon "Rick's Café" (of the movie, *Casablanca*, fame)

The Moscow Marathon

One of my favorite experiences has to be running the Moscow Marathon. It was 1988, before the Berlin Wall had come down, and suspicions between the Soviets and the U.S. ran deep. I decided that since I hadn't died from cancer yet and my vegan diet seemed to be working, Moscow was going to be my next marathon. I found while running the streets of Moscow that Russians were intensely curious about Americans; they were also very friendly, and usually knew enough English to carry on a decent conversation.

I'd heard of the idea of taking the "Aloha" spirit in the form of orchids to pass out during runs, and I'd managed to get five thousand orchids shipped from Hawaii to Russia. Fortunately, once I explained what I was trying to do, the agricultural departments, customs, and airlines of both countries cooperated. Even the hotel provided a refrigerator in which to store the flowers until the day of the marathon.

Three of us divided up the prize and we must've looked strange, toeing the starting line with large bags of orchids on our backs. Once the gun went off, we started passing orchids out to each person lining the course, which included Soviet soldiers acting as course marshals. I could tell from their stony-faced expressions that this was a duty they didn't relish—standing at attention, making sure that no one strayed from the course, not knowing how long it would take for the last runner to pass, and realizing it was probably more hours than they'd been told it would be.

As I ran up to each of the soldiers, I'd make sure I had a big smile on my face as I handed him an orchid and said, "Aloha from Hawaii!" I was met with not much of a reaction and thought, *Gee, this isn't working very well*. After I related the experience to my translator, she said they probably couldn't understand what I was saying. There is no "h" in the Russian language and their word for Hawaii is "G-vai." From then on I pronounced it "G'vai," and each recipient of an orchid nodded his head and smiled. Ah, the importance of communication.

So when people say to me that running is boring, I say "No way"!

The Zen of Running

As you may have discerned by now, I tend to over-cerebrate and see running as a problem to be solved as much as an experience to be enjoyed. Unlike the purists, I often run with propulsive pop music pounding in my ears as opposed to listening to the sounds of nature (or the Brooklyn–Queens Expressway, at least), and take to the treadmill rather than brave the byways and back roads of my borough.

Nonetheless, I can appreciate how running can take you out of yourself—and not solely because the longer distances offer you as much of a psychopharmacological trip as a physical one. In the races I've completed without musical enhancement stimulating my auricles, I've come to appreciate a different sound palette: the pat . . . pat . . . pat . . . of feet hitting the pavement at the same pace as you run through a sparsely populated area at mile eighteen; the roar of the crowd as you come off the Queensboro Bridge at mile sixteen and turn onto First Avenue in Manhattan; making it to the summit of the legendary Heartbreak Hill in the Boston Marathon, knowing how many others have struggled up it, too. Quiet satisfaction may not be as sexy as enlightenment, but it has its place among life's pleasures.

What running races *does* make me aware of is the resilience of the human spirit even though it may be enclosed within a body that does not or cannot operate with maximal utility. I refer, of course, not only to the handcyclists or wheelchair competitors, but the Achilles athletes who are blind or visually impaired and are accompanied around the course by another athlete, attached to a string. Or Zoe Koplowitz, who's completed twenty-two New York City Marathons since 1987, even though she has multiple sclerosis, and it takes her over thirty hours from start to finish. She holds the record for last place—a feat that isn't merely a testament to the hardiness of someone who each year attempts to move twenty-six miles and change on crutches, but a critique of a world that appears to value speed more than endurance, getting ahead rather than looking around, youth more than age, and the harnessing of ability rather than freedom *within* disability. Seen within the broader frame of the body in motion rather than the narrower conception of the athlete, running becomes not about winning or losing but an elemental acknowledgment of our frailties and our strengths as magnificently complex motile beings. As Ruth suggests, in such a reconceptualization of running we have the opportunity to recapture (however briefly) the sheer joy of being alive.

—M.R.

Running Is Lonely

"Running should be a lifelong activity. Approach it patiently and intelligently, and it will reward you for a long, long time."

—**Michael Sargent**, runner

For many non-runners, running sounds like a lonely endeavor. The sight of a single runner out in the country does make one wonder. And, yes, sometimes it *is* lonely. In a strange new town where you don't know a soul, you might go out for a run just to see other people. What no one observes, however, is what's going on in the runner's head. For example, I've gone out for runs to explore a city I just arrived in, or sometimes to formulate a solution to a problem, and even at times to lessen my frustration over a perceived slight.

But the best solution by far is to find somebody to run with. And that's where running clubs can save the day, where you most likely can find a compatible running friend—or two or three or more!

Running Clubs

After fourteen years of solitary running, I got serious about my training when I decided I was going to do the Ironman Triathlon. Knowing I needed a coach and guided training, I checked around and found two such groups. One of them was Faerber's Flyers, a group of women-only runners coached by legendary University of Hawaii track coach Johnny Faerber, winner of a silver buckle given to those who complete the Western States 100-Mile race in under twenty-four hours. This group started in the late 1970s, and although Johnny Faerber no longer coaches, several dedicated volunteer coaches still show up every Wednesday, rain or shine. We worked out on the University of Hawaii track once a week, and here I had the opportunity to improve my speed.

The second group I joined was coached by another legend, Max Telford, who holds a Guinness World Record for running 146 miles across Death Valley in 56:33 hours and enduring temperatures that have been known to reach 134°F. He accomplished this incredible feat in 1982, the same year of my cancer diagnosis and subsequent turnaround in my own life. I figured he'd be just the one to help me get to the long distances I'd needed to do well in the Ironman, which had a cut-off time for completion of seventeen hours.

I joined both clubs and got serious about both speed and distance and found great support from these two groups—and not just from the coaches but the other runners as well. It made track workouts and long Saturday runs fun as well as effective.

A few years later I found myself on the other end of groups. Because of my interest in health and fitness, I'd studied for and passed the test to become a Certified Personal Fitness Trainer. After about ten years of competitive running and racing triathlons, I was offered the chance to coach people who wanted to train to run marathons or triathlons. It was great fun to pass on some of the joys of running and racing that I'd experienced and to see "newbies" flourish and share in their triumphs as well.

Distance Running

Many runners become "hooked" by running longer distances. Once we've mastered the 5K, we move on to the 10K. Then comes the half-marathon, and from there, there's the tantalizing, full 26.2-mile marathon. I can tell you that, after more than sixty of them, I still feel an indescribable thrill crossing the finish line. It's a mix of joy, maximum empowerment, relief, wonderment, and either "Just wait until the next time!" or "That's it! I'll never do another one!" For many of us, the latter feeling may last only until our recovery is complete, for it's then that the pain of "hitting the Wall" is lessened. For many, all that remains is a joy that's like nothing else.

Another advantage that distance running has for us as we age is that it takes not only a good deal of fitness to do these events, but also a certain level of maturity. In my judgment, the first three-quarters of any race is physical and the last quarter is mostly mental. It seems to require a willingness to bear a lot of discomfort and a level of patience that youngsters usually haven't developed. This is why older runners can still take home lots of "hardware." Plus, if you play your cards right, you'll outlive all your competition!

Races also serve a charitable function. You've doubtless noticed that many runs raise awareness or money to cure breast cancer or leukemia, or help the homeless, and other worthy causes. Being able to serve an organization with goals that you want to support provides a motivation to train. It also provides the opportunity to get a lot of non-runners involved, especially friends or relatives who'd probably never otherwise consider taking part in an event of this type. If they have a positive experience, they'll no doubt be back for more.

There's also the bonding that comes with pushing yourself to new heights with others doing the same. It's hard to explain, but there's nothing like the kinship that occurs between runners who share hopes, goals—and a lot of pain. There's something magical that happens when we accomplish something we never thought possible before. Just watch the faces of finishers as they cross the finish line at marathons or ultramarathons. It can bring them—and you—to tears.

The Tarahumara of Mexico

Have you ever heard of the Tarahumara people? Their name comes from *Raramuri*, meaning "running people." They are truly long-distance runners, not because they necessarily want or need to prove themselves, but because they've been pushed by "civilization" from their homes into the rugged Copper Canyons of Mexico. Food is hard to grow where they live, so they eat mostly corn and squash—a primarily vegan diet. When traveling, which is always on foot, they carry a cloth pouch of ground corn, which when they are hungry, they mix with water. The children start running at a very young age; in fact, as soon as they can walk. A commonly played game consists of kicking a ball between two teams, and can go on for up to forty-eight and seventy-two hours, until the last person left standing is declared the winner.

The Tarahumara are the original barefoot runners as well. No $150, hi-tech running shoes for them! They scrounge up old tires, cut them into the shape of their feet, string some rope through three holes punched into the soles, and then wrap the rope around their ankles. They have won major ultramarathon races, such as the Leadville Trail 100 Run (which is, as its name suggests, one hundred miles long), wearing just these on their feet. One runner was fifty-five years old when he came in first!

I first read about the legendary Tarahumara and their 24- to 48-hour races around 1999 and decided that some day I would have to check these people out in person. Shortly after that, I happened to receive a travel brochure in the mail for a tour through the Copper Canyons in northeastern Mexico, where we would visit with the Tarahumara. I immediately signed up and was soon heading to see some of the world's best runners.

We rode by train to Divisadero, a town in the Mexican state of Chihuahua, not far from where the Tarahumara lived deep in the canyons. We were met at the train station by women (and some men) selling copper jewelry, baskets, and other souvenirs. These peoples' English was nonexistent, so asking where the runners were got me nowhere. Nor was our guide much help because, although he was Mexican, he knew very little about these people's running exploits. Luckily, he asked around and the next morning a group of the Raramuri had assembled.

It was quite a conglomeration of folks, clad in loose tops and loin-cloths, some quite elderly. But what immediately caught my eye was their shoes. Yes, they really were made from old tires and twine. As the men ran back and forth along an open clearing, I joined them. They seemed surprised but readily accepted this "gringo" runner, probably wondering why I would want to run with them when none of the other tourists ever did. Little did they know how much I admired their running and especially their vegan diet! (The Tarahumara are the subject of Christopher McDougall's *Born to Run*.)

Getting a Trainer

To my dismay, after many years of steadily improving times, and following a personal best in Miami in January 2011, my next three marathons (New Jersey, Chicago, and New York) saw me stumbling in at 3:50 and change. I was hitting the Wall—and not just hitting it, but slamming into it head first. Everything would be going swimmingly until mile eighteen and then my legs would feel heavy and, more ominously, the Negatives would start up with their drone: *Why are you running this race? What have you left to prove? It's boring; just stop.* I had to find a way to get back to the physical *and* mental state of just a few months earlier.

So I hired a trainer, a wonderful woman by the name of Martha Prakelt. Martha is boundlessly enthusiastic, fully committed to the personal and physical well-being of her clients, and a generous and decent person dedicated to making the world a better place for human and non-human alike. I told her my goal, which was to get back into shape for three Fall marathons in 2012 and return to what I wanted my default time to be: 3:30 (or thereabouts). Martha set me up for track work once a week. I ran 400 meters at ninety percent effort, followed by a 200-meter walk/jog, and did so seven or eight times, and then over the following eight weeks graduated to 800 meters at ninety percent effort, followed by a 200-meter walk/jog, five or six times. I practiced core strength training (push-ups, planks, and bicycle kicks) and undertook some upper-body weightlifting. We also completed forty-five minutes of spinning once a week.

The track work was intended to give me a kick of speed toward the end of a race. The strength work was meant to make me, well, stronger. The spinning was the sort of cross-training that exercised parallel muscles but didn't over-strain those used in running. It was up to me to make sure I got my running mileage in every week, and to complete four or five long runs (eighteen miles or more) to rebuild my stamina so that the Wall wouldn't be so high or I wouldn't hit it so hard the next time.

More significantly, Martha and I knew that one of the goals of the ten-week training was to put me in a better frame of mind—one that didn't fret about the long runs that would ultimately count in preparing my body for glycogen deple-tion. She advised me to give myself a mantra and internally to vocalize positive thoughts throughout the race as a way of disciplining the mind to silence the Negatives and free it from over-thinking a situation. As it turned out, I came down with bronchitis a week before the Chicago Marathon and had to be content with 3:34 on the day, which was still a full quar-ter of an hour faster than my time the previous year. New York was canceled; but six weeks after Chicago, I came in at 3:30 in the Brooklyn Marathon.

As I navigated the undulations of Prospect Park, I felt great. What surprised me, even as I ran it, was my attitude toward the steep hill that leads toward Grand Army Plaza—a half-mile-long, three-percent gradient I had to ascend *six* times. Each time, I leaned slightly into the slope, shortened my stride, pumped my arms from the shoulders, and tried to tread gently on the ground—all techniques that Martha had prescribed for running up slopes. But it was the fact that the slope held no terrors, that I felt mentally strong and capable, that was key to my time. Mile twenty was in essence no different from mile eighteen or mile twenty-two, and the Wall nowhere to be seen. It certainly helped that Martha was at the top of that steep hill, cheering me on.

Any trainer should provide you with the physical pointers you need to achieve your goal and push you to complete the program. What Martha recognizes is that a substantial part of becoming a successful runner (whatever that might mean for you) is about being in good psychological condition: one that is both a cause and effect of the discipline and practice of correct training. If or when you look for a trainer to help you reach your goals, make sure they understand the mental side of running. It's more important than you might think. —*M.R.*

There's No Such Thing as a "Runner's High"

"Running long and hard is an ideal antidepressant, since it's hard
to run and feel sorry for yourself at the same time."

—**Monte Davis**, runner

H*a! Gotcha on this one! What we commonly think of as* a "runner's high" *is* a myth. A lot of runners most of the time, especially beginning runners, feel anything *but* a runner's high as they drag their butts through some designated distance. The good news is that there is scientific evidence to support the existence of a "runner's high"—if, and only if, you're fit enough.

At the University of Arizona, a team of researchers measured brain chemicals associated with increased pleasure called endocannabinoids in humans before and after running sessions on treadmills.[30] They found that humans had a significant increase in endocannabinoids after bouts of high-intensity endurance runs. The researchers concluded that there is a neurobiological reward, the so-called "runner's high," for endurance at a high intensity. They also concluded that inactive people may not be fit enough to hit the required intensity that leads to that "reward." The two factors influencing the release of endocannabinoids are intensity and duration, a minimum of twenty minutes.

What about the opposite of a high? If you've suffered from depression or have known anyone who has, you know that it's a major problem that can have devastating results. Antidepressants, which affect levels of mood-regulating serotonin in the brain, are often prescribed to treat this condition. Studies have shown that, in some people, antidepressants provide minimal improvement and can have risky side effects, including risk of suicide. As published in the May 2012 issue of the journal *Frontiers in Psychology*, Paul W. Andrews and his associates pointed out that there is minimal benefit, along with a laundry list of negative effects such as diarrhea, constipation, indigestion, bloating, abnormal bleeding, strokes, sexual dysfunction, and more. Another study concluded upon review of the antidepressant literature that initial improvements are often followed by resistance to treatment and worsening depression. On the other hand, we know that exercise is an effective way to increase serotonin levels in the brain, which can ease depression.

Running Can Help Addictions

Statistically, people who exercise are much less likely than inactive people to abuse drugs or alcohol. But can exercise help curb addictions? Some research shows that exercise may stimulate reward centers in the brain, helping to ease cravings for drugs or other substances.

Justin Rhodes at the University of Illinois and Martina L. Mustroph published in *The European Journal of Neuroscience* their research on addictions and exercise, and "how profoundly exercise affects learning."[31] What the addict requires to overcome an addiction is to learn new, more healthful habits. "Fundamentally, the results are encouraging," Dr. Rhodes says. "They show that by doubling the production of robust, young neurons, exercise improves associative learning." These findings underscore that these new cells are indiscriminate and don't care what you learn. They will amplify the process, whether you're memorizing Shakespeare or growing dependent on nicotine, none of which, Dr. Rhodes says, should discourage people from exercising or from using exercise to combat addictions.

A number of studies by other researchers show that exercise seems to be able to stimulate reward centers in the brain that can substitute for drug cravings. "It's a no-brainer, really," Dr. Rhodes concludes. "Exercise is good for you in almost every way." But it is wise to bear in mind, he adds, that by exercising "you do create a greater capacity to learn, and it's up to each individual to use that capacity wisely."

Beyond the Finish Line

Contrary to sedentary America's belief, lifelong running is good for us in many ways. Once, when I was invited to give talks at Stanford University, I managed to do a few races at the same time and found that there was research being conducted on this very subject.

James Fries, M.D., coauthor of a 2008 study from Stanford University that tracked 528 runners and 423 non-runners beginning in 1984, counts the ways: "Running improves your blood pressure. You're less likely to get blood clots and varicose veins. Bones become stronger and denser. It's a treatment for osteoporosis. It prevents fractures of the hips and spine. The ligaments get bigger and stronger—they protect the joints from wobbling, which is one thing that causes joints to wear out. Lungs get stronger. Our physical reserve is greater."[32]

The Stanford study confirmed what we lifelong runners have always suspected:

- Runners suffer fewer disabilities. Running delays age-related disabilities by almost two decades.
- Runners are seven times less likely to require knee replacement.
- Running does *not* lead to increased hip, back, or knee problems.
- Runners suffer less cancer and fewer neurological problems.
- Runners are half as likely as non-runners to die early.

Runners began the study with an average of 12,000–14,000 miles on their legs, and many have since doubled that. So most of us aren't just weekend joggers. Some are Olympians. "Running is a very natural thing," says Fries, "and there's no upper limit to it, as long as it's not painful."

I'm delighted to say that I am one of the runners being followed in this study.

Spot the White Guy

Spend any time distance-running, even in as racially diverse a city as New York, and you'll being to think . . . that running is something that only white people do—except, of course, for the elites at the front of the pack. As continued success on the track has borne witness to, athletes of color are well-represented at the shorter distances. But, apart from people like the remarkable Ted Corbitt (1919–2007), one of the founders of the New York Road Runners and pioneer of ultramarathons, elite African American marathoners remain a rare breed.[33]

This phenomenon hasn't gone unnoticed: New York Road Runners has programs in areas of the city whose majority population is of color, in order to encourage young people to get involved in running. The organization Black Girls Run (www.blackgirlsrun.com) has chapters throughout the country, as does the National Black Marathoners Association (www.blackmarathoners.org). Running authorities point to American champions like Meb Keflezighi, Abdi Abdirahman, and Desiree Davila as inspirations for young men and women of color to recognize that you don't have to be African to win races, or simply to take part.

The need to get *all* communities to exercise is, as Ruth has suggested, not only a matter of saving lives but of reducing health care costs. We've already discussed the consequences of obesity on an individual's overall well-being, but it's worth emphasizing how critical the situation has become within communities of color, particularly among African Americans. According to statistics from the U.S. Department of Health and Human Services Office of Minority Health:

- African American women have the highest rates of being overweight or obese compared to other groups in the U.S. About four out of five African American women are overweight or obese.
- In 2010, African Americans were 1.4 times as likely to be obese as Non-Hispanic Whites.
- In 2010, African American women were seventy percent more likely to be obese than Non-Hispanic White women.
- In 2007–2010, African American girls were eighty percent more likely to be overweight than Non-Hispanic White girls.

The percentages for obese children (ages 6–17 years) were even more alarming: 14.6 percent of Non-Hispanic White children were obese compared with 25.7 percent of African Americans (2009–2010 figures). That means a quarter of black children are obese, not just overweight. Now, as we've discussed, you don't have to be beanpole thin to be healthy or a runner. But when obesity is at such epidemic levels, cultural claims about full-bodiedness being an act of resistance against unrealistic or undesirable body types simply aren't adequate as a response. (I've only quoted a few of the statistics available from the Office of Minority Health; as a whole, they make very alarming reading.)[34]

Of course, as the social media reactions to the cancellation of the 2012 New York City Marathon revealed, all too painfully, perceptions matter. Whether those of us who run like it or not, running (and running marathons) is seen by some as essentially an indulgence for the middle-class and well-to-do—a result of too much time on our hands and money in our pocket. We may protest that we're running races for the most altruistic of causes. Yet I suspect that even the money raised for charity and the inspiring stories that many runners bring to the races may, in some quarters, only confirm the notion that runners are do-gooders disconnected from the harsher realities (and indignities) of being the recipient of that charity, or of being ignored altogether because one doesn't *look* like one can take care of oneself.

As a middle-aged white guy who's frequently found himself clustered comfortably within a pack of middle-aged white guys in marathons, I'm surely not alone in feeling like I'm one of ten thousand clones, all seeking some form of personal redemption! That sense is only enhanced when you're spectating at one of the big marathons. I always ask my support posse to tell me where they'll be standing so that I can look out for *them*, and not the other way round. As a spectator, it's impossible to make anyone out, even if they're standing and waving their arms in front of you, when all you've seen for the past hour is wave after wave of pale-complexioned men flowing past you in an endless tide of self-improvement.

The health of our nation is a serious matter, and so is any perceived or actual exclusion of groups of people because they don't feel comfortable or accepted at the starting line— for whatever reason. As the winners' podium in races around the world bear witness to, no one ethnicity has any biological handicap that stops them either from competing at the very highest level or trundling around the course like the rest of us. Although all communities (rich or poor, of any color) are guilty of self-policing what activity is acceptable or unacceptable for "people like us," it's up to the running authorities and every one of us to do what we can to make the experience of running as open, affordable, and attractive as we can. As Ruth has suggested, the future of the United States may depend on it.   —M.R.

CONCLUSION

In order for our civilization to survive, we need a healthy population. Almost everywhere I go, I see sickly, unfit, obese people. From what we know of neuroscience, our brains are dependent on being supplied with the right nutrients and good circulation. That's certainly not what our population is getting.

How are we going to be able to solve the major threats we face today, such as global warming, terrorism, political gridlock, deforestation, the collapse of the ocean's ecosystem from overfishing and pollution, and the loss of sufficient farmland to grow our food, without a population who can think its way out of these threats? I'm really concerned about the health of our next generation, with so few people getting enough exercise and eating a poor diet. We must turn this around before it's too late, and I believe the first step is physical fitness.

As for myself, after more than forty years of running, I can still say that for the most effective and efficient exercise, nothing beats running. It can be done most any time, anywhere, in any kind of weather, and in just about any part of the world. I believe that these basic attributes qualify running as closest to the perfect exercise for most people. From the Great Wall of China to bridges like the Sydney Harbour Bridge and the Golden Gate Bridge; from Nepal, Norway, Korea, Japan, New Zealand, Oman, Mozambique, Estonia, and Namibia; running has given me as much pleasure as fitness. It strengthens my bones as well as my muscles; it keeps my heart strong; it increases the oxygen-extracting efficiency of my lungs; and I invariably feel much happier after a run than when I started. Not once have I ever said at the end of a run, "Gee, I wish I hadn't done that." It's always, "Gee, I'm so glad I did that!"

Someone once asked me how many miles I've run so far in my many years of running. The idea intrigued me, so I came up with this estimate. If I averaged six miles a day for forty-five years, the total comes to 98,550 miles. That's the equivalent to almost four times around planet Earth. That fact alone gives me a feeling of accomplishment and satisfaction along with the tremendous level of fitness that I still enjoy. Who can ask more than that of any one exercise? Not me! Running is the closest I've come to discovering "The Fountain of Youth."

APPENDIX

've known a number of people who've started out as non-runners and become runners over time—some late in life and for many different reasons. Some are famous and known worldwide but most are just everyday people who run. Here are just a few of their stories. Hopefully, you'll find them as inspiring as I did.

Randy Kreill

Life can change fast, just when it seems most everything is going your way. In September 2004, at age forty-two, after experiencing speech difficulty at my ninety-five-year old grandfather's funeral service, I saw my doctor with a suspected case of "sinusitis." She found a tangerine-size thyroid gland and was surprised we hadn't noticed it before! She'd given me a full physical exam three months prior. The X-ray was ugly, showing a grossly misshapen windpipe.

By chance, I had just finished reading about a famous young athlete's uphill battle with cancer. The size of my lump, along with his story, spooked me into three consecutive nights of no sleep. A top-rated surgeon was guessing it wasn't cancerous, but he was wrong, forcing two surgeries in three weeks.

When I asked the surgeon how a relatively healthy guy gets Follicular Thyroid Cancer, he looked up and said, "For all we know it falls out of the sky." Needless to say, that answer was too vague. I sensed it was BS. My yearlong journey to minimize any future cancer risks began, with many baby steps along the way, such as weight loss, improved diet, and more exercise.

"When the student is ready, the teacher will appear" is a Buddhist proverb that comes to mind. My multiple reads of the bestselling book *Born to Run* by Christopher McDougall led to some coincidences that put Ruth Heidrich in my life at precisely the right time (December 2010). I'd always been intrigued by the Ironman Triathlon, but I was not an athletic young guy and only a mid- to back-of-the-pack runner/ sprint triathlete in my late twenties. That was progress for a kid who had done no team sports from middle school through college.

In *Born to Run* I learned of superhero endurance athletes performing on a hundred-percent plant-powered diets, and I learned about Ruth's plant-based solution to metastatic lung and bone cancer. So, intrigued to see if the local Heidrichs were related to her, I contacted her about using "her" diet to finally get off cholesterol meds and lessen future cancer risk. Ruth quickly taught me what I needed to know, and I found the cholesterol-free, vegan diet to be easy, delicious, portable, and affordable.

And, yes, Ruth was the grandmother to a local guy, as I suspected she might be! I'm still working toward more whole foods. We're all a work in progress. I easily keep a healthy weight and have learned to run 50K (thirty-one miles and beyond) nearly barefoot. The benefits of a plant-strong diet go on and on. My vision has improved. My recovery times are much shorter from longer and often faster workouts, and it's been about seven years since I've been to the doctor with an illness. The seven years coincides with the time frame where I cut way back on dairy products. Ruth had me "flipped" out of the Standard American Diet (SAD) in about one week. Shortly afterwards, I was off my cholesterol medication and running beyond marathon distances!

I recently hit fifty years old and now look forward to a good probability of being vibrantly active very late into my senior years. Now that I'm "Re-Born to Run" on a hundred-percent plant-based diet and feeling great, I'd love to pay it forward by letting as many people as possible know about my positive results, along with Ruth's story and others.

Prevention is the key word. It can be tough to get people interested in these ideas before a crisis. Vegan endurance athletes like Ruth literally and figuratively grow larger hearts, creating a strong desire to help others. Ample healthy motion, in combination with a diverse hundred-percent plant-based diet, represent the "twin fountains of youth" to this vegan barefoot endurance runner who is looking forward to going further, faster, and having more fun.

Speaking of fun, for my fiftieth birthday on August 25, 2012, I set up a full Ironman-distance personal triathlon locally, which meant a lake swim of 2.4 miles at Caesar's Creek Beach, a bike ride of 112 miles, and a 26.2-mile marathon, which my wife ran as her first full marathon run. Our three daughters cheered us on with friends and family, and we had a custom finish that was very memorable. It was 15½ hours of fun! Why let travel costs, scheduling, and entry fees keep you from going the distance? Create your own adventures!

Lastly, I now believe Ruth is absolutely correct. DIET is the four-letter word that trumps everything else. We are meant to run, and everything we do to become better at running helps us feel more human, happier, healthier, and more resilient. To run better, eat better. What I would call an upward spiral can start just about anywhere. I've found that if I eat better, I run further, faster, and crave even healthier food, while recovering faster and avoiding illnesses. When I then deliver the healthier foods to satisfy my body's cravings, I then run even more. Swimming and biking are great, as they make me a better runner. Who wouldn't want that?

—*Randy Kreill*
Beavercreek, Ohio

Bob Leitch

1964

At age twenty, I'd noticed I had gained some weight, and since I'd heard that you could lose weight by running, I decided I'd give running a try. At the time, my parents, my brother, and I were living in a small desert town in southern California, so one evening I took off away from town and headed down to the end of a nice, lonely road. I found I really enjoyed the calm, peaceful feelings and the desert scenery. I did this three or four times a week for a couple of months and gradually built up a fair amount of mileage. When I lost the weight, I quit running.

1971

Having just finished the final requirements for my master's degree, I had been under a lot of stress and smoking too much. When my best buddy and I were out relaxing out by the football field, he came up with this crazy idea. He suggested we take off our shoes and go for a run. I thought, *Why not? What a way to celebrate our academic accomplishment!* We started out on the grass of the football field and continued on to the trails that were next to the campus. We must have run ten or eleven miles, and most of what I remember is being very stiff and sore for the next several days.

1978

I had just gotten a new job, was still smoking, and was really out of shape. At age thirty-four I decided to turn over a new leaf and went out and bought my first pair of running shoes. My first run out, I lasted about a quarter of a mile before my chest began heaving and I started tasting blood. I turned around and walked back. Three or four days later, I tried it again but got further this time before turning around and walking back. Over a period of several weeks, I was able to gradually increase my distance to eight miles.

1982

I was still smoking, and I was still continuing to run. But in the spring of 1982, I lost my job. I became very depressed and fell into a very unhealthy lifestyle and stopped running.

1986

Turning over another new leaf in January, I started running again. During a lunch hour, I went to the local gym to lift weights and soak in the sauna afterward. That was when I met Ron, who was running with a group that was training for the May 1986 Vancouver International Marathon (he trained with the group on weekends, but on his own during week-nights). He encouraged me to join him three times a week to train at the end of our workdays. Seems like I went from zero to sixty! Through rain, snow, ice, hills, intervals—we did it all! I had gotten up to long runs of eighteen miles when I got injured. Despite being told to quit running, I cut my mileage way back, got some physical therapy, gradually got my mileage back up, and did my first half marathon in August 1986.

1990

Crazy as it sounds, I was still smoking. It wasn't until the end of the 10K Vancouver Sun Run in April 1990 that I quit smoking. Ron and I had just finished that race, and I pulled out my cigarettes from my training pack and lit up. Ron looked at me and said, "I can't believe you're still smoking." Up to that time I had rarely smoked in front of Ron, so he was shocked that I'd been doing all this running and was still smoking. At that point, I looked down at the cigarette, looked at Ron, and decided I had to quit (like many other smokers, I'd quit many times before). This time I was able to quit, and stay so! I haven't smoked since April 1990 . . . and I'm still running smoke-free and strong.

1995

In the Fall of 1990, my wife was diagnosed with terminal brain cancer. We desperately tried every treatment, every doctor, and any and every alternative anybody came up with. None worked, and after she died in October 1995, I fell into another depression. I stopped running and turned to food to stuff the feelings. I started eating a horrible, junk-food diet and gained more than sixty pounds.

1996

Still in that unhealthy lifestyle, I developed DVTs—deep vein thromboses (blood clots)—in my left leg. I was hospitalized in February, put on blood thinners, and was told I'd have to take them for the rest of my life because they could easily be fatal when the blood clots traveled from the leg to the lungs—a pulmonary embolism.

1997

I hated taking the blood thinners, so I quit. However, I then got another bout of DVTs. I returned to hospital, was put on the pills again, and was told the same thing: that I'd have to take them for the rest of my life, and I'd better not quit again—or else!

1998

Lying on the couch depressed and sorry for myself, I had a bucket of fried chicken and half a gallon of ice cream to console myself. I was channel-surfing on my TV, looking for something to distract me, and came across Ruth Heidrich giving a talk on healthy diets and the many benefits to be gained from running. She also mentioned that animal foods tended to sludge the blood and that vegan diets kept the blood nice and thin. I did some research, thought I would like to give it a go, and checked with my doctor. "Forget it!" he said, immediately. "It won't work for you." He continued that if I went off the blood thinners, he'd "fire" me as his patient. "I don't want you dying on my watch!" he told me.

More research, however, convinced me that it was worth a try, and I finally found a doctor who agreed to monitor me as I changed my diet and started running again—on one condition, that I take an aspirin a day. After six months of perfect blood tests, I was told that my new vegan diet and running were obviously working and that I could even drop the aspirin. I've been a vegan runner ever since.

1999

Dr. Ruth showed me that I was capable of running more than three times a week. I learned to run, injury-free, seven days a week. And with the vegan diet, my recovery time was so much quicker that I soon learned that I could even run back-to-back races. Ruth also showed me the training that I needed to do to complete a triathlon. In August 1999 I did my first and only triathlon (so far).

I'm not someone who likes swimming (having nearly drowned on four separate occasions when I was a youngster). So, when I completed that triathlon (in Honolulu), and was told afterward that during the swim portion of the triathlon I was swimming above hammerhead sharks, I freaked out. It was a good thing that no one mentioned the sharks *before* the triathlon or I'd never have gotten in the water!

Although I had run in some races before I met Ruth, I'd never won anything other than a finisher's T-shirt. Ruth showed me that I could run faster and even competitively. Not too long after she and I started training together, I began to place in my age-group—winning numerous ribbons and trophies. What a hoot! What a thrill! It certainly made running a lot more fun—even though it unleashed a bit of the competitive "beast" I didn't know I had in me. Sometimes that "competitiveness" put undue stress on me, and took a bit of the fun out of some of the races.

After many years, going through several injuries and practicing the "active recovery" process that Ruth promotes, I'm still running, and I even enjoy it. I've settled into a pattern that works best for me right now and feels most comfortable. I'm now only running three times a week, and each run is approximately 10K (6.2 miles). The other three days of the week, I lift weights. And on the seventh day I rest. (Hey, if it's good enough for some biblical deity, I figure it's good enough for me.)

I've put my competitive "beast" back in the shadows as I no longer race (for the time being). I'm happy to be alive and simply enjoying stress-free and injury-free running. I'm contented to have had a diverse, challenging, and interesting running history—one that has been so enriched by Ruth, who not only saved my life, but also taught me how to find so much more abundance in life through a vegan diet and the rest-of-my-life-long running.

—*Bob Leitch*
White Rock, British Columbia, Canada

Diamond Lil

I'm a happy, energetic seventy-one-years-young retiree who feels very youthful and enjoys life. I started running just days before my seventieth birthday. I had been diagnosed with osteoporosis sixteen years before and had been put on pills for nine years, which gave me constant stomach pains. So doctors put me on intravenous infusions for six years. I'd played sports most of my life and had been walking for years. Yet I'd never even considered the possibility of running.

Being interested in my health and wanting to live a long, healthy life, I read articles on Ruth Heidrich in our local paper and read her book *Senior Fitness*. I then realized that with my osteoporosis that I had to take action to get off the pills and infusions, which I did and started running—slowly at first, and gradually increasing the distance.

My early mornings start off with stretching, and I can't wait to begin my run—with a smile on my face and no more stomach pain. I also use dumb bells when I exercise at home for my upper body and take them on all my road trips. I don't leave home without them!

About four months into my running, my husband, Bob, and I were house sitting five kilometers from a small town when I decided I would try and run in. As a backup, I told my husband to give me a half an hour and then drive into town to see if I needed a ride. I actually made it to our meeting place before he did, and some friends cheered me on as I came in for the home stretch. What a great feeling of accomplishment—five kilometers!

I also realized how important my diet was and thought I ate very healthfully. I used to call myself a vegetarian but still ate wild salmon and free-range chicken until I starting doing some research and found out this wasn't healthy at all. I was eating eggs and dairy but found out this might have been causing osteoporosis. So I changed our diet to fruits, vegetables, whole grains, beans, and nuts, and, luckily Bob agreed. Aged seventy-one, he skied seventy-nine days last year and feels stronger than ever.

We're very satisfied, happy, have lots of energy, and haven't felt this good in years. Neither one of us is on any drugs, which means no side effects. Sometimes my friends ask me for some of my energy. I tell them that it doesn't happen on its own. Exercising and eating healthy contributes to my high energy level. When I was young, I told myself I never wanted to be overweight. Well, I haven't been and have never had to go on a diet. I aim to stay on this lifestyle for the rest of my life. We're glad we made the switch to healthier eating and know we still have lots of years ahead of us.

Thank you, Dr. Ruth. You have been such an inspiration. Hopefully, I can keep on running for many more years and encourage other people as well. It's never too late!

—*Diamond Lil*
White Rock, British Columbia, Canada

Lance Peverley

She asked me why I was running. But I had no answer; I didn't know what makes me run. Others have said they've seen me training. I'm not. I'm jogging. Long distances. But, I protest (too much, perhaps), I'm most definitely not into training. I don't even care what route I take. I just like to run. It empties my mind.

The thing is, nature must abhor an empty mind.

A few weeks back, as I made my way along the winding Nicomekl River, I glanced over at the golf course where my father was its first club president. A sense of pride beat along the trail that sweltering Saturday afternoon. Back westbound on the serpentining Crescent Road, memories of Dad teaching me to drive were equally vivid.

Down the hill, past the church basement that served as my kindergarten, I passed our old house at the railway crossing and rounded the corner toward Blackie Spit, where I took my own children kite flying this past spring.

My mind was jumping months, years, and decades with every few steps through Crescent Beach. I passed the pier where I fished for bullheads in my youth, a grassy area where I served as a best man years later, and the bed-and-breakfast where I filmed an episode of *The X-Files* during my Hollywood North period.

Heading back inland, I noticed the site of the long-gone corner store where I ran errands for my mother at age four—a different era, to be sure—and met the boy who instantly became my BFF.

I jogged past the house where I met my soon-to-be beloved, past the school annex that would serve as our makeshift chapel (and, sadly, to where I returned years later to remove my ring after finding out "forever" rarely is), and toward Ocean Park, where my father and brother worked at the same grocery store, decades apart.

Passing the community hall where I did my best as a Cub Scout, I glanced at Kwomais Point, where I was a camper, a counsellor, and a first-day assistant director on the feature film, *Dudley Do-Right*.

Eastbound on Marine Drive, I looked at the many homes I had visited along life's journey, realizing that these and other memories have always been there. They just needed a little nudge.

Down into White Rock, past my first house—rented by my parents for $50 a month—past the barbecues and train station, a rapid series of events and faces popped into my mind. I stopped at the pier for a few seconds to wait my turn at a water fountain, and looked up toward the big house on the hill where a friend's mother—one of White Rock's kindest longtime residents—had passed away the day before. The seconds turned into a moment, my sweat into tears. . . .

A deep breath, and I was off again—past the rock, where I climbed; past the pub, where I socialized; and toward the now-fenced-off park, where I served as bat-boy on my father's ball team.

There, my journey went uphill fast, just before the site of the old house where I rented a bedroom in the nineties. Forget my history, that house—constructed for sawmill workers—had been around since the First World War, until it made way for the future just a couple of years ago.

Up the hill. Legs slowing. Head spinning. Body hurting.

My pastime was losing its allure.

I looked up and noticed Peace Arch Hospital. Where my father and two grandparents had died. Where my three children were born. Where life, too, began for me. And I realized I must continue to run. And why the route is as important as the destination.

—Lance Peverley
White Rock, British Columbia, Canada[35]

ACKNOWLEDGMENTS

Someone once said, *"We are today what we will be in* five years except for the people we meet and the books we read." This is certainly true in my case. I owe a huge debt of gratitude to Kenneth Cooper, M.D., for his 1968 groundbreaking book, *Aerobics*. This book launched me on a running adventure that has provided me with innumerable health benefits (literally from head to toe), the pleasure of seeing the world (much of it on foot), and the challenges and joys of running races.

The second person to whom I owe another huge debt of gratitude is John McDougall, M.D., who I can safely say saved my life. His clinical research into the role of diet in breast cancer gave me the opportunity to contribute to breast cancer research and to add diet to the other half of my health equation.

Having made these two momentous discoveries, I went charging off on a mission to save lives. It wasn't long before I discovered that very few people were ready to hear what I'd found out from these two pioneers. Gradually, the running movement took hold, and I was meeting other runners, none of whom felt their diets needed improving. I later met others who had changed their diets but could not imagine themselves as runners. I found the lack of progress in my mission frustrating, to say the least.

Then along came Martin Rowe, editor at Lantern Books, who became a great ally with the power of his press. In addition to publishing my first two books, *A Race for Life* and *Senior Fitness*, when I hit over forty years as a runner, he came up with the idea of a book on lifelong running, the result of which you are holding in your hands. It is an effort to distill forty-five years of experience into something worth reading.

Then came Wendy Lee, whose job it was to take these all-over-the-map musings and whip them into a logical, readable, convincing, and hopefully spellbinding prose that will convince you, the reader, of the merits of this healthy lifestyle of running on a vegan diet.

I thank you all!

RESOURCES

Books and Films

Brazier, Brendan. *Thrive: The Vegan Nutrition Guide to Optimal Performance in Sports and Life* (New York: Penguin, 2007).

Dreyer, Danny and Katherine Dreyer. *ChiRunning: A Revolutionary Approach to Effortless, Injury-Free Running* (New York: Touchstone, 2009). An excellent book on running form.

Dunham, Jon (dir.) *Spirit of the Marathon* (Calico 1880, 2007).

———. *Spirit of the Marathon II* (Calico 1880, 2013).

Ehrlich, Judd (dir.) *Run for Your Life* (Screen Media Films, 2008).

Egoscue, Pete and Roger Gittines. *Pain Free: A Revolutionary Method for Stopping Chronic Pain* (New York: Bantam, 1998). An approach to running injuries that looks at possible causes such as postural imbalances and how to correct them.

Heidrich, Ruth E. *A Race for Life: The Amazing Story of How One Woman Survived Breast Cancer to Take on the Toughest Races in the World* (New York: Lantern Books, 2000)

———. *Senior Fitness: The Diet and Exercise Program for Maximum Health and Longevity* (New York, Lantern Books, 2005)

Jurek, Scott and Steve Friedman. *Eat and Run: My Unlikely Journey to Ultramarathon Greatness* (Boston: Houghton Mifflin Harcourt, 2012). A memoir by the vegan ultramarathoner.

McDougall, Christopher. *Born To Run: A Hidden Tribe, Superathletes, and the Greatest Race the World Has Never Seen* (New York: Knopf,

2009). The story about the Tarahumara and the research done at Harvard University on the evolutionary aspects of human running.

Murakami, Haruki. *What I Talk About When I Talk About Running* (New York: Knopf 2008).

Robbins, Liz. *A Race Like No Other: 26.2 Miles Through the Streets of New York* (New York: HarperCollins, 2008).

Roll, Rich. *Finding Ultra: Rejecting Middle Age, Becoming One of the World's Fittest Men, and Discovering Myself* (New York: Crown, 2012). An incredible midlife physical transformation through diet and exercise.

Other Resources

Active.com <http://www.active.com>. A website that lists races in your community as well as everywhere else.

American Medical Athletic Association <amaa@multibriefs.com>. A newsletter that provides excellent information on the role exercise plays in a healthy lifestyle.

Black Girls Run <http://www.blackgirlsrun.org>. Running organization for African-American women.

Marathon Guide <http://www.marathonguide.com/>. A list of all the marathons around the world by month, with comments from runners on each race.

Martha Prakelt <http://marthaprakelt.com/>. Martha Prakelt, personal trainer.

National Black Marathoners Association <http://www.blackmarathoners.org/>. Self-explanatory.

New York Road Runners <http://www.nyrr.org/>.

No Meat Athlete <http://www.nomeatathlete.com/>.

NYC Runs <http://nycruns.com/>.

NY Runner (the magazine of New York Road Runners).

Runner's World <www.runnersworld.org>.

Ruth Heidrich <http://www.ruthheidrich.com/>. Ruth Heidrich's website.

Triathlon Today <https://sites.google.com/site/triathlontoday/>.

NOTES

1 Ehrlich, Judd (dir.) *Run for Your Life: The True Story of Fred Lebow and the New York City Marathon* (Screen Media Films, 2008).

2 Information about the study is featured on pp. 220–228 of Christopher McDougall's *Born to Run* (New York: Knopf, 2009).

3 Dawkins, Richard. *The Selfish Gene* (New York: Oxford University Press, 1989).

4 Klingamen, Mike. "Women Outnumbering Men on Race Day," *The Baltimore Sun*, October 12, 2012.

5 Kolata, Gina. "See Jane Run. See Her Run Faster and Faster," *New York Times*, August 30, 2007. See also the opinions expressed in "Marathon and a Half Really Rocks," by Don Norcross, *San Diego Union-Telegraph*, June 1, 2010.

6 A full-throated defense of barefoot running can be found in McDougall, *Born to Run*, op. cit. pp. 168–183.

7 Hall, C., Figueroa, A., Fernhall, B., & Kanaley, J.A. Energy expenditure of walking and running: Comparison with prediction equations. *Medicine in Science and Sports and Exercise* 2004 Dec:36(12):2128–34.

8 *European Society of Cardiology* (2012, May 3). Regular jogging shows dramatic increase in life expectancy [Press release]. Retrieved from <http://www.escardio.org/about/press/press-releases/pr-12/Pages/regular-jogging-increases-life-expectancy.aspx>.

9 Ibid.

10 Clark, P.J., Brezezinska, W.J., Puchalski, E.K., Krone, D.A., & Rhodes, J.S. (2009). Functional analysis of neurovascular adaptations to exercise in the dentate gyrus of young adult mice associated with cognitive gain. *Hippocampus* 2009 Oct; 19(10):937–50.

11 Aberg, M., Pedersen, N.L., *et al.* Cardiovascular fitness is associated with cognition in young adulthood. *Proceedings of the National Academy of Sciences (PNAS)*. Article PNAS # 09-05307, Dec. 2009.

12 Teri, L., *et al.* Exercise plus behavioral management in patients with Alzheimer's Disease. *The Journal of the American Medical Association* 290(15):2015–2022. (Oct. 15, 2003).

13 Gustafson, D., *et al.* An 18-year follow-up of overweight women and risk of Alzheimer's Disease. *Archives of Internal Medicine* 163(13):1524–1528 (July 14, 2003).

14 Cooper, Kenneth. *Regaining the Power of Youth at Any Age* (New York: Thomas Nelson, 1998).

15 Quoted in Strange, Carolyn J. *Boning up on osteoporosis*. DHHS Publication, No. (FDA) 97-1257. (Rockville, Md.: Dept. of Health and Human Services, 1997).

16 Hagobian, Todd A., and Braun, B. Physical activity and hormonal regulation of appetite: Sex differences and weight control. *Exercise and Sport Sciences Reviews* 38.1 (2010): 25–30.

17 Lin, S.W., Wheeler, D.C., Park, Y., Cahoon, E.K., Hollenbeck, A.R., Michal Freedman, D., & Abnet, C.C. Prospective study of ultraviolet radiation exposure and risk of cancer in the U.S. *International Journal of Cancer* 2012 Apr 26. doi: 10.1002/ijc.27619.

18 Sorenson, Marc. *Solar Power for Optimal Health* (self-published, 2006).

19 The article is featured in "Fighting Jet Lag with Scheduled Exercise," by Alex Hutchinson, *Runner's World*, April 9, 2012.

20 Ibid.

21 See for instance <http://www.cdc.gov/nccdphp/dnpao/hwi/toolkits/stairwell/motivational_signs.htm>.

22 Clancy, Carolyn M. (2009, April 7). *Comparative effectiveness*

research: What it means for you. <http://www.ahrq.gov/consumer/cc/cc040709.htm>.

23 Sharma, P., Maffulli, N. Tendon injury and tendinopathy: Healing and repair. *The Journal of Bone and Joint Surgery* 87:187–202, 2005. doi:10.2106/JBJS.D.01850.

24 "Mike Fremont, 91, Finishes Knoxville Half Marathon in 3:04," by Michelle Hamilton, *Runner's World*, April 8, 2013 <http://www.runnersworld.com/races/mike-fremont-91-finishes-knoxville-half-marathon-304>.

25 For more on the New York City Marathon, see *A Race Like No Other: 26.2 Miles Through the Streets of New York*, by Liz Robbins (New York: HarperCollins, 2008).

26 Belson, Ken. "Behind the Scenes, a Race of Logistics," *New York Times*, November 5, 2010.

27 Macur, Juliet. "Plodders Have a Place, but Is It in a Marathon?" *New York Times*, October 22, 2009. See also "Running with Slowpokes: How Sluggish Newbies Ruined the Marathon," by Gabriel Sherman, *Slate.com*, September 22, 2006.

28 Parker-Pope, Tara. "A Marathon Run in the Slow Lane," *New York Times*, November 2, 2009.

29 McDougall, Christopher. "Born to Run the Marathon," *New York Times*, November 4, 2010.

30 Raichlen, David A., Foster, A.D., Gerdeman, G.L., Seillier, A., & Giuffrida, A. Wired to run: Exercise-induced endocannabinoid signaling in humans and cursorial mammals with implications for the 'runner's high.' *The Journal of Experimental Biology* April 15, 2012, 215:1331–1336.

31 Mustroph, M.L., Stobaugh, D.J., Miller, D.S., DeYoung, E.K., & Rhodes, J.S. Wheel running can accelerate or delay extinction of conditioned place preference for cocaine in male C57BL/6J mice, depending on timing of wheel access. *The European Journal of Neuroscience* 2011 Oct, 34(7):1161–9.

32 Chakravarty, E.F., Hubert, H.B., Lingala, V.B., Fries, J.F., Reduced disability and mortality among aging runners: A 21-year

longitudinal study. *Archives of Internal Medicine* 2008; 168 (15): 1638–46.

33 See for instance, "Changing The Face of Distance Running," by Nick Patowski, *Runner's World*, January 4, 2008 <http://www.run-nersworld.com/runners-stories/changing-face-distance-running>.

34 The U.S. Department of Health and Human Services Office of Minority Health: Obesity and African Americans <http://minorit-yhealth.hhs.gov/templates/content.aspx?ID=6456>.

35 Originally published as "Memories Jogged, One Step at a Time" in *Peace Arch News*, White Rock, British Columbia, Canada. Reprinted by permission of the author.

ABOUT THE AUTHORS

RUTH HEIDRICH received her PH.D. in Health Management in 1993, is a six-time Ironman Triathlon finisher, and is the author of *A Race for Life, The Race For Life Cookbook, (CHEF),* and *Senior Fitness.* She is a certified fitness trainer and holds three world records for fitness for her age group at the renowned Cooper Clinic in Dallas, Texas. She still actively competes in marathons and triathlons, having won more than 900 trophies and medals since her diagnosis of metastatic breast cancer in 1982 at the age of forty-seven. She is a founding member and past president of the Vegetarian Society of Hawaii and past president of the Mid-Pacific Road Runners Club. She has won eight gold medals in the Senior Olympics in Hawaii, Arizona, and Nevada, and was named one of the "Ten Fittest Women in North America."

MARTIN ROWE is the author of *The Polar Bear in the Zoo, The Elephants in the Room,* and *The Bugs in the Compost.* He is the editor of *The Way of Compassion* and the founding editor of *Satya: A Magazine of Vegetarianism, Environmentalism, Animal Advocacy, and Social Justice.* He is also the author of *Nicaea: A Book of Correspondences,* co-author of *Right Off the Bat: Baseball, Cricket, Literature & Life,* and the co-founder of Lantern Books. He lives in Brooklyn, New York, and is fond of running marathons to raise money for causes he supports.

ABOUT THE PUBLISHER

LANTERN BOOKS was founded in 1999 on the principle of living with a greater depth and commitment to the preservation of the natural world. In addition to publishing books on animal advocacy, vegetarianism, religion, and environmentalism, Lantern is dedicated to printing books in the U.S. on recycled paper and saving resources in day-to-day operations. Lantern is honored to be a recipient of the highest standard in environmentally responsible publishing from the Green Press Initiative.

www.lanternbooks.com